More Horse Calls

A Dream Fulfilled

D1547298

Marcia A. Thibeault, DVM

More Horse Calls

A Dream Fulfilled

The events described in this book are true, but the characters are composites of several people, and the names have been changed to protect their privacy.

ISBN 978-0-9817848-1-6

Published in the USA by
Medicine Beau Ink
P. O. Box 1702
Georgetown, Kentucky 40324

To order additional copies of I Make Horse Calls or More Horse Calls send $14.95 per copy plus $4.95 s&h to the above address or visit our website at www.imakehorsecalls.com

.

A portion of the proceeds from sales of this book will be donated to create a scholarship for a student enrolled in the Colorado State University College of Veterinary Medicine.

Printed in the United States by Morris Publishing
3212 East Highway 30
Kearney, NE 68847
1-800-650-7888

This book is dedicated to my family.

My mother, Catherine, lives her life as an example of unconditional love. She shared her interest in science, thoroughness and lifelong pursuit of learning.

My Father, Irv, who taught me how to work with my hands.

My Grandmother, Kitty, and Great-Grandfather, Tom, taught the value of dedication, hard work, and persistence.

Thanks to the talented horsemen and women, professors and veterinarians who helped me along the way, and the faithful, loving animals that shared my life.

Prologue

Since I first set eyes on a horse as a toddler, a bond was formed that would never break.

When I was a young child, peering out the back window of our car, if I spied a pony ride, I'd beg my parents to stop and let me ride. I'd gladly hand over the entire contents of my piggy bank to ride until my meager savings was gone.

The smell of the ponies, their glistening coats and long manes and tails, the clip-clop of their hooves, their beautiful brown eyes - the windows to the spirit within - all captured my soul.

As a teenager my bond with animals, especially horses, grew steadily stronger. I wanted to - I needed to - spend my life around these wonderful, inspiring creatures. And when I found people who shared my passion I let them into my inner circle, for it was a special kinship, inexplicable to those who lacked it.

No matter what obstacles lay in my way, nothing would deter me from that goal.

My life would be forever enriched by horses. By caring for them my dreams came true.

Chapter 1 A Little Bit of Help

My big, beautiful Rocky was going to be okay!

I was so grateful he had turned the corner. I continued to visit him at the university hospital. After seven days in intensive care the IV was removed, but he stayed in the hospital for another three days to see if his kidneys would work without the help of IV fluids. It was touch-and-go, but finally his condition was stable and he was ready to come home.

When I visited the hospital for the last time I thanked everyone for their help, as it clearly was a team effort to save Rocky's life and I was so grateful. Seven veterinarians, 29 veterinary students, and countless vet techs worked around the clock to save him. They were intelligent, educated, compassionate individuals, and I appreciated their help. I could never have provided that level of care by myself.

The trip to the business office was not as painful for me as I had feared. It took all of my savings, but no more. While the bills at a referral hospital are never small, veterinary medicine is a bargain when compared to human medicine, yet the standard of care is as high in veterinary medicine as in human medicine. Blood tests and diagnostic equipment cost the same, whether used for human or animal patients. Medications cost the same, but the dose must be increased six fold to treat a 1000 pound patient versus a 150 pound human, at six times the cost. Lapses in sterile procedure that lead to infections are just as deadly in veterinary patients as human patients.

Veterinary medicine rendered at a teaching hospital is the best bargain of all, because the students pay tuition while working around the clock, supervised by vets who mentor them. I recalled attending patients during night duties when I was a student, not that many years before. The level of care Rocky received was unparalleled. His life had been saved by these devoted caregivers.

And I could not have provided around the clock care for Rocky for ten days straight. I would have had to cancel my clients' appointments, which would have cost more than Rocky's bill and stay awake for ten days. Nor did I have the best equipment or rapid turn-around on lab tests. The expertise of so many students and specialists - radiologists, toxicologists, internal medicine experts, clinical pathologists, ultrasound technicians - all worked together for the benefit of patients at the university teaching hospital.

Be that as it may, my "rainy day fund" was now gone, again, but I couldn't think of a better use for it.

As I drove Rocky home, I reviewed the preparations I'd made for his return. It was too cold to leave him out overnight in the small, sandy paddock where he lived before he became ill. During the day he would be turned out. The loafing shed would shelter him from the winter winds, but at night he would have to come inside, so I prepared a stall for him in the barn that would become my vet clinic when time and money allowed the improvements to be completed.

I had already removed the unsafe barn wiring but in the meantime we'd be freezing in the dark.

So I bought a heavy duty, outdoor extension cord and ran it from the house to the barn. It would run lights, but no heat. Any water in the barn would freeze overnight, so I'd carry a bucket of steaming hot water around midnight to top off Rocky's bucket. That would ensure unfrozen water throughout the long cold nights. Horses need fresh water available at all times, but for an animal with kidney disease, it's a matter of life and death.

Rocky always began shedding his winter coat in January, and this year was no exception. Increasing length of daylight triggers shedding and he had been under lights 24 hours a day at the vet hospital because the vets need light to monitor their patients around the clock. This February the weather was bitterly cold, with highs barely creeping above ten degrees, and the winds were brutal, sweeping down the Front Range and exploding across the prairie. The days were sunny, but the nights were frigid. High altitude and low humidity with no cloud cover meant the heat the ground absorbed during the day dissipated quickly after sunset.

I had some heavy horse blankets, but Rocky never liked them. He refused to eat from the ground when I put a blanket on him. The pressure the blanket put on the base of his neck bothered him when he reached down for his hay.

We got home before dusk, so I put Rocky in his paddock and parked the trailer in the shed. He seemed content and relaxed. A pleasant roll in the sand removed the smell of the hospital from his coat, replacing it with the scent of home. He whinnied to the neighbor's mares, and they returned his greeting. I was glad to have him back. By the time I cleaned and unhitched the trailer, daylight was gone, so I brought Rocky into the barn. I groomed him in the barn regularly, but he had never spent the night inside before.

His stall had a feeder hanging on the wall, so I filled it with hay and put two horse blankets on him, a slippery, nylon one underneath that should slide easily across his skin and, and a heavy insulated one on top for warmth. He had lost his insulating layer of fat and most of his winter coat. It was critical he eat enough calories to keep his body temperature up to normal. He had to wear the blankets.

I went to the barn every few hours to adjust his blankets, but he had little interest in eating.

If he wouldn't eat, he wouldn't live.

I had to motivate him to eat.

The barn had no windows on the side where my neighbor's mares were pastured. He was isolated. He needed the shelter of the barn, but he was so alone. I had to get him a companion.

Some skittish show horses travel with goats, or burros, or ponies, but at the moment I only had Rocky and Clancy. Rocky needed a companion that would not bring any diseases onto the farm. An infection could kill him in his weakened state. And I needed a horse that would not injure him, as he was so weak.

Wherever Rocky had been boarded he was always the alpha dominant leader of the herd. Any new horse might test him and one of them could be injured. As a vet I had humanely destroyed a number of horses that broke their legs in kicking duels. I couldn't take that chance with Rocky.

I had to find a special horse - a friendly, healthy non-threatening companion. As I dropped into bed at midnight, after taking Rocky his warmed water, I drifted off to sleep. But instead of counting sheep, I mentally reviewed my list of patients... and I found the perfect horse - actually, she was a pony.

I had a dear client, Barbara Lewis, who is such a wonderful lady. She and her best friend, MaryAnn Morrissey, stabled their horses together at MaryAnn's farm. Two kinder souls have never walked this earth. They were always helping out worthy causes. MaryAnn worked as a nurse, and volunteered for the Red Cross, while somehow finding time to help Barb care for her horses. Barb volunteered at the animal shelter, and cared for the high-maintenance animals no one else wanted.

Barb helps as many animals as she can - dogs, cats, horses, burros - any animal that needs a safe haven at her home. Barb had certified her Schnauzer, Mitzy, to visit human patients in hospitals to cheer them up. Her Islandic pony, Little Bit, could fill the same role for Rocky.

I knew Little Bit well from caring for her. Barb had her animals on my best preventative medicine program, so the pony was healthy. Little Bit was so small Rocky's alpha status wouldn't be challenged. And if she did kick, she wouldn't pack much of a punch. She was gentle and Rocky liked mares. She was my best hope for Rocky's companion.

Now all I had to do was convince Barb to lend me her pony. I'd call her first thing in the morning. We were both up early tending our animals.

In the morning I cleaned Rocky's stall, re-filled his feeder with hay, although he had not eaten his full ration, and gave him a scratch on his belly. He did not pull away today and he seemed glad to see me. I slipped the halter over his huge head to take him out.

"I'll put you outside before I go on rounds today, but you'll need to come inside at night until it gets a little warmer. And I may have a surprise for you."

I know it's crazy to talk to animals, but that has never stopped me.

Clancy and I walked up to the house to call Barb. She should also be done with chores by now.

It was nice to hear her voice when she answered the phone.

"Good morning."

"Good morning, Barb. How are you and your critters today?"

"Fine, just letting the dogs out. Hang on a second while I get Mitzy....Okay, I'm back. What can I do for you? Is Rocky okay?"

"Yes. He's doing okay, but he could be better. Because it's so cold, I have him blanketed and in the barn at night. But he's isolated from my neighbor's mares when he's inside. He hates the blankets and isn't eating much overnight. He's lost so much weight and his insulating layer of fat is gone. I'm worried about him. He eats when he's outside during the day, but it was so cold last night I couldn't leave him out."

"No, you can't leave him out in this cold weather. I wish I could help."

"As a matter of fact, you can. Or rather, Little Bit can."

"What...?"

"Well, you know how Mitzy cheers up patients in hospitals?"

"Yes....but I don't think Rocky would like a visit from a Schnauzer, do you?"

"No, but he'd probably love a visit from Little Bit!"

"You've got to be kidding."

"No, I'm dead serious."

"Well, I'd never thought of hospital visitors for equine patients, but if you think it'd work, I'm willing."

Barb was such a dear!

She brought Little Bit over that afternoon.

Little Bit had been foundered, a painful condition that had permanently scarred her hooves, and she needed medication every day. The medicine was bitter. I tell my clients to make medicating their horses as pleasant as possible by mixing the medicine with applesauce because it's easy and horses like apples. But when Little Bit arrived at my farm, she came with her medication and jars of baby food -Dutch Apple Delight.

Barb always went the extra mile for her animals.

Rocky was glad to see Little Bit. When I put her in the paddock next to his, he immediately came over to the fence and nickered quietly to her. She was more interested in investigating the new territory.

"Looks like she's playing hard to get, isn't she?" remarked Barb.

"Yeah, but he sure likes her."

After Barb left I went up the house for dinner. Clancy was glad to have two horses to guard now, although she stayed by Rocky.

After dinner I mixed up the medication for little Bit. When I opened the jar of baby food, I was amazed at how savory it smelled, much better than my applesauce. I might have to start recommending this for all of my patients. I was tempted to try the Dutch Apple Delight myself and give Little Bit her medicine in my applesauce. Naw, that wouldn't be right.

Clancy and I walked down the gravel drive to the paddock and gave Little Bit her medicine. The mare saw me coming, and immediately raised her head, opening her mouth to get her "treat." This was going to be easy. From that day on, she just rested her muzzle in the crook of my left arm while I squirted the paste in her mouth. Even Rocky thought he might be interested in some.

Little Bit's stall in the barn had been prepared with fresh water, a flake of hay and deep pine shavings. Haltering Rocky, I took him out of the paddock first. I didn't want to lead the two of them together in case either one objected to the other horse in close proximity. It could be dangerous to lead two horses that didn't know each other. As I closed the door behind Rocky and went to get Little Bit, Rocky started whinnying at the top of his lungs. He was calling to Little Bit. Apparently he had already bonded to her.

I brought Little Bit into the barn and put her in the stall directly across the aisle from Rocky. The stalls had solid fronts, but the doors had bars on the upper half, allowing circulation of light and air. When I closed the stall door behind us I saw she was too short to reach the hay in the feeder, so I put her hay on the ground. When she put her head down to eat, she was so small Rocky couldn't see her through the top half of the stall door. To compound the problem she was a dark bay, and in the dark confines of the barn, with the daylight quickly fading, I could hardly see her at all even when I was standing right next to her. I didn't want to leave the lights on all night, but I considered it to reassure Rocky that he was not alone.

I left Little Bit in the stall and finished closing up for the night. I put Rocky's blankets on him. As I looked into Little Bit's stall from Rocky's, I could see her craning her neck to see what I was doing. She could barely get her eyeball above the top of the door. And all I could see was the white of her left eye.

Rocky had watched her go into the stall, but when she put her head down to eat, she disappeared. Rocky began munching contentedly on his hay, but every few minutes he would stop and listen, ears twitching for any sound. Although he couldn't see Little Bit, he could hear her eating. Once he heard her, he'd resume chewing.

When I came down with hot water all was quiet. Little Bit was down in the shavings resting, having quickly consumed her ration and Rocky had already eaten more hay than the entire previous night. He was content. My plan was working.

By the next morning Rocky had finished all of his hay, and looked a bit brighter. I led them outside separately, with Clancy's assistance, but put them together in the same paddock. There was a little sniffing and nickering, but soon all was quiet. I went up to the house for breakfast, but kept a watchful eye on them through the kitchen window as I scheduled the day's appointments. Little Bit disappeared into the shed, but Rocky stood in the doorway. Before I went on my day's rounds, I checked them again. Little Bit was lying in the deep bed of shavings, and Rocky was by her side, standing guard like a big brother. Their contented expressions convinced me that Rocky was on the road to recovery.

I went on my day's rounds and finally my mind was at ease.

That night I led them into the clinic together. There would be no fighting between this pair.

After a few days I turned them out in the pasture together. As his strength returned he was ready to walk around more. The first few blades of spring grass were appearing, and Rocky savored every one as it emerged.

As the days went by, I kept Barb informed of the marvelous transformation Little Bit was making in Rocky's attitude. Barb came to see Little Bit when she could, and brought graham crackers for her. Little Bit loved them. Rocky began begging for some as well. He patiently rested his head on my shoulder while I opened the packages for him. It was good to see him take an interest in treats again. He had been through so much.

"He looks better, doesn't he?" Barb remarked the first time she came out.

"Yes, your little miracle worker helped save his life!"

"Well, I don't know about that."

"Well, I do. Medicine can only take a patient so far. The patient has to want to get better, and now he does."

When Dr. Mom returned from vacation, she wanted to help Rocky recover, so she also bought graham crackers for him. But her conservative nature caused her to pick generic graham crackers, instead of the more expensive brand Barb bought. I hurriedly opened the box while Rocky waited for me to hand him one. But when he discovered they weren't his favorite brand, he quickly and disgustedly spit them out!

Mom offered the unopened portions to Dad, who willingly ate them.

Over the next few months Rocky looked better, regaining the weight he lost. I watched from the dinner table as he trotted and cantered around the pasture. The weather was turning mild and he could spend the night outside in sight of my neighbor's mares, so I returned Little Bit to Barb. I was confident Rocky would be okay without her.

Rocky's life was saved due to the efforts of so many talented veterinarians and vet students, and one marvelous pony with a kind-hearted owner.

Rocky whinnied for his new friend when I returned with the empty trailer. They had bonded in their short time together. When he was healthy food always made him feel better, especially the lush grass of spring, so I took Rocky to hand graze in the rear garden with Clancy as his bodyguard.

Horses are so attuned to their environment. They won't eat if they are ill or upset by anything around them. Ever since I was a child, I found the sound of a horse's chewing relaxed me. As a vet I know a horse that won't eat means a medical problem for me to solve.

So as Rocky grazed in the garden today, his massive jaws grinding the grass in a slow, rhythmic song, the sound penetrated the depth of my soul, bringing an overpowering sense of peace.

Chapter 2 Too Hot to Handle

Since the day I struck out on my own, I was afraid to leave my practice for even a day, lest I lose the opportunity to gain a new client. But after many months of being on call 24/7, I took my first vacation.

For my birthday my sister got us airline tickets to fly to Lexington, Kentucky to see the Rolex Three Day Event. This international competition combines dressage, a cross country jumping and endurance course, and stadium jumping into an all around test for equine and human athletes.

The trip had been marvelous. As we flew low over historic Calumet Farm on the way to Bluegrass Airport, I fell in love with Kentucky - the beautiful rolling hills, green grass, ancient oak trees, manicured horse farms and incredible horses.

We spent most of our time at the Kentucky Horse Park, a thousand acres of prime bluegrass devoted to the horse - showcasing breeds and hosting competitions of all types. We toured the Hall of Champions which displays retired racing Thoroughbreds and Standardbreds. We spent hours in the International Museum of the Horse, which highlights the relationship between horses and humans and showcases collections of equine art. The Breeds barn presented live shows of a dozen breeds of horses every day. In addition, there were exhibits of saddle making, horseshoeing, and carriage driving.

We toured Keeneland, a beautiful race course which is also the site of one of the most prestigious horse auctions in the world, and the filming location for the movie "Seabiscuit." We went to

Lexington's harness racing track - The Red Mile. It was Lady's Day and we were given free admission and red carnations.

What a wonderful vacation it had been! Someday I would return.

As my pager jarred me from my daydream, I realized I was home, the vacation was over, and it was time to go back to work.

The page was from Paul Pointer. His Arabian mare, Spicy, developed a slight cough when I was gone. Now she had hives. In my absence he had purchased penicillin at the feed store, and called Dr. Melton, who had agreed to take emergency call for me, to ask him how much penicillin to give Spicy.

This creates a problem.

The Veterinary Practice Act makes it illegal for veterinarians to prescribe any medication for a horse without first examining the animal. The examination establishes a doctor/patient relationship, from which all diagnoses and treatments arise. Unfortunately, it is legal for tack shops and feed stores to sell some veterinary medications to horse owners, without prescriptions. Owners assume medications available over the counter are safe, but that's not always true.

I don't prescribe antibiotics for horses without examining them first. If the horse needs antibiotics, it needs an exam and a diagnosis to determine if the drug will be more beneficial than harmful. When the owner, without benefit of a veterinary education, makes the diagnosis and chooses the treatment, I get nervous. All drugs have the potential for complications, and penicillin is noteworthy for its fatal complications in some horses, so it should only be used if the horse will reap significant benefit from its use.

Dr. Melton tried to get Paul to schedule an appointment, but he refused, asking again for the dose. Reluctantly Dr. Melton gave told him. Spicy would not be overdosed, but did she need antibiotics?

Paul felt the mare had done better after a few injections, and gave her the last dose on Friday evening. It was now Monday night, and the mare had hives. Paul, again making his own diagnosis, decided the hives were a reaction to the penicillin and called me.

"How's she acting?"

"She's normal - eating and drinking. She just has hives."

"While hives can be a sign of an allergic reaction, allergic reactions to penicillin usually are rapidly fatal. So Paul, if the last dose of penicillin was three days ago, penicillin is not the cause."

Horses can get hives from insect bites or proteins in the diet, and usually the hives go away without medication, although treatment can make the horse more comfortable and shorten the recovery time. I told Paul that if he felt it was an emergency, I would come this evening, but if she seemed normal otherwise, I would see her in the morning.

He was comfortable waiting until morning, so we scheduled an appointment for nine o'clock.

At six o'clock the pager disturbed my restful sleep.

It was Paul.

"I just went out to feed and Spicy's hives are much worse, Doc. She's really sick. Can you come out *now*?"

"I'm on my way!"

What could be causing Spicy to have hives and be so sick Paul wanted me right away?

I climbed in the truck, but had little time to think about Spicy's problem. Paul's farm was nearby and I was soon there.

Racing from my truck to the paddock I was shocked by Spicy's appearance. She had no ordinary case of hives, which usually consisted of a few dozen small, raised skin bumps around a horse's neck and chest - every inch of her entire body was covered with hives two inches in diameter. Her skin was engulfed with one continuous hive.

When I laid my hands on her I could feel she was burning up with fever. The thermometer confirmed my findings - 105.4. She couldn't tolerate this high temperature for long without suffering serious complications. Paul had been right - Spicy was very ill.

I had no time to figure out the cause of the problem, I had to treat the symptoms right now! I hurried through the rest of my exam.

Her pulse was racing - normal is 30, hers was 100.

She was breathing very rapidly, five times the normal rate. But her lungs were moving plenty of air, and free of fluid. She didn't have pneumonia, or an upper respiratory infection.

She wasn't eating. She could barely catch her breath.

Her gums were pink, with no hemorrhages.

"Paul, this mare is really in trouble. I have to get her fever down, and fast. She's in danger of permanent injury from the fever. After we get her fever down we'll figure out the cause. I'll begin some IV medication, but you need to hose her down with cool water to drop her temperature. Get your hose right now."

I gave Spicy two IVs - an anti-inflammatory medication and a broad spectrum antibiotic with virtually no side effects.

To find the cause of an infection it's best to take a sample of the infected tissue, from an abscess or nasal discharge, and send it to the lab to identify the bacteria. Sensitivity tests then determine which antibiotics will work. But in Spicy's case I had no idea where the infection was. There was no abscess or runny nose to sample. But even if I chose the wrong antibiotic, the fever reducers and hosing should buy her some time.

Because hives are a sign of an allergic reaction, I also treated Spicy with antihistamines. Steroids are stronger, but if I gave her steroids when she was fighting an infection, she could get worse. Steroids depress the immune system meaning the infection might kill her. I opted for antihistamines now, knowing that if Spicy didn't respond I could resort to steroids after she had a few doses of antibiotics on board.

"Keep her away from the other horses, in the barn and out of the hot sun."

It was June, and the high altitude sun was very strong. Spicy couldn't risk any further increase in body temperature.

Paul moved her to a shady spot near the house and began hosing her.

I drew a blood sample for a panel of tests. I would carry the blood straight to the diagnostic lab and order the tests run STAT.

"I'll stop by first thing tomorrow morning and see if our treatments are helping her. Take Spicy's temperature tonight and call me. If she takes a turn for the worse, call me right away."

Paul had four children. I knew his family would be devastated if we lost Spicy.

I dropped the sample at the lab and in a few hours they called with results. To my dismay, the results were normal. I was glad Spicy's blood didn't reveal internal organ failure, overwhelming infection, or anemia, but I knew she certainly wasn't normal! It's so difficult to win the battle when I can't identify my opponent.

In veterinary school, the professors made it seem so simple to reach a diagnosis. Just do a thorough physical exam, and perhaps run blood tests or take an x-ray, and the diagnosis would be obvious. While many cases are that simple, there are plenty of sick horses with normal test results.

Paul called that evening saying Spicy's temperature was down to 102.5. I was relieved.

The medications were working, and for the moment the mare was out of danger from the fever, but I was no closer to knowing the cause of the problem.

When I stopped by Paul's farm in the morning, I was pleased to see that Spicy was brighter, but a look at her legs immediately ended my delight. Her legs had swollen to twice their normal size - so swollen the skin had split open and was oozing serum.

I cleaned the wounds and wrapped her legs in antiseptic bandages. A thick layer of ointment covered with a small sheet of plastic wrap would hold in the moisture and body heat. I was careful as I placed the plastic so it didn't constrict blood flow. I then applied thick cotton bandages. The bandages would reduce the swelling and the risk of infection. Her immune system had all it could handle fighting an unknown foe, and didn't need any more infections.

A complication of respiratory infections called Purpura hemorrhagica can cause a horse's legs to swell, but Spicy did not have the severe respiratory infection that usually precedes Purpura. She also didn't have the hemorrhages in her gums that are seen with Purpura. In addition, Spicy had the worst case of hives I had *ever* seen, and hives were not reported to be part of Purpura.

It was critical to get the swelling under control right away, so I gave the mare steroids and a diuretic to remove the fluid. I didn't know which medication had reduced her fever, so I continued the antibiotics. Giving Spicy five drugs at the same time made me nervous, because there could be complications from drug interactions. I had never done it before, but she was so sick she needed all of them. This game little mare was fighting for her life, and I did everything I could to help her.

Paul had not let his kids come to the barn at feeding time, fearing they might find her dead. Spicy was still in danger, but I was encouraged since her temperature was down. I took a urine sample and submitted another blood sample to the lab, but again the results came back normal.

The next morning Spicy's temperature was nearly normal. The bandages were loose because the swelling was down. She showed no new symptoms. She was more interested in eating, and seemed to be moving around her stall comfortably since her legs were less swollen. Her hives had shrunken noticeably.

I rebandaged her legs and adjusted her medications. I told Paul she had probably turned the corner. Whatever was making Spicy sick - we were beating it.

Paul's farm was my first stop the next morning. His children and wife were in the paddock when I drove in. They told me Spicy was feeling much better, and at sunrise she began whinnying loud enough to wake the entire family. She wanted her breakfast!

As they watched her, she tossed her long red mane playfully, trotting up and down her shady paddock, demanding that she be fed immediately. They happily obliged.

But something was still not right. In the dim light of the early morning, I needed a closer look. Spicy had changed colors. The chestnut mare was now a mousy gray. Her bright red hair had fallen completely out, revealing the gray skin beneath. Every single hair on her body was gone, except her mane and tail! I'd never seen a horse go bald overnight.

I shared the family's joy at Spicy's recovery, but cautioned Paul to keep her out of the sun until her new coat grew in, so she wouldn't get sunburned.

Whatever caused the allergy was never determined. Spicy probably reacted to a weed in her pasture. There were poisonous plants in the pasture, but none showed signs of grazing and Paul's other horses were healthy.

The mystery remains unsolved, but Spicy recovered.

Paul's kids outgrew Spicy and she was sold.

The last time I saw Spicy she had just completed a 25 mile endurance race, and she looked fit enough to cover another 25.

Chapter 3 A Little Knowledge Can be Dangerous

I was on call for Dr. Melton when I received a call early one morning from his client, Bob Tyler. One of his daughter's Quarter Horses, Scotch, had cut his face and needed stitches. I got directions and told Mr. Tyler I would be right out. He lived on the other side of Denver, so traffic would normally be a problem, but it was so early I could be there before rush hour got into full swing.

I thought this call would be a piece of cake. Facial lacerations were usually simple and straight forward. They heal with minimal scarring, and they are on a part of the horse's body I can reach without going through major contortions. And I was perfectly suited for repairing lacerations, because my childhood hobbies were needlepoint and jigsaw puzzles. Once I figured out where the pieces went, all I had to do was sew them back together.

I pulled into Mr. Tyler's farmyard and saw his sorrel gelding tied to a horse trailer. The house was a neat, sprawling brick ranch house, with a large bank of flowers gracing the hillside. The flowers were well tended, and the east facing slope caught the morning sun. The irises were in full bloom.

I try to keep an upbeat attitude, as clients are often upset at the prospect of their horse suffering an injury, and at the unexpected expense of my services. I would compliment Mr. Tyler on his beautiful flowers. Or maybe a joke would ease the tension.

Mr. Tyler was not in a joking mood.

"Good morning Mr. Tyler. I'm Dr. Thibeault. How are you today?"

19

"I've been better. I spent the weekend re-roofing Scotch's stall to keep him dry and comfortable, and somehow he must have reared up and found a sharp edge on the metal roofing to cut his face. So I tied him to the trailer while I was on the phone with you, and he got tangled in his rope, fell down, and he cut his leg under the trailer."

He was definitely not having a good day.

"Oh, my. I'm sorry. I hope it gets better from here."

"Can't get much worse."

Mr. Tyler was an older gentleman, well groomed, and dressed in a business suit. He had risen early to feed the horses before he left for work, and Scotch's injury was making him late.

"I'll get you on your way as soon as possible."

"I'd appreciate that. I changed from my chore clothes to my office clothes so I could leave for work as soon as you were done."

I went about my job, examining Scotch without any small talk. None of his wounds were serious. I cleaned and sutured them, although my knees were aching by the time I finished sewing up the leg wound and bandaging it. I left Mr. Tyler antibiotics to give Scotch, and some medicine to keep the swelling down.

"Call Dr. Melton's office tomorrow. He'll need to come out in three days to change the bandage, and then in two weeks to remove the stitches."

"Why aren't you coming back?" he asked angrily.

"I only cover emergencies for him. He is still your regular veterinarian."

Dr. Melton and I had an arrangement that we would handle emergency calls for each other, but we never stole clients from one another. We refused to do follow-up appointments once the client's regular veterinarian was available, so the client would have to return to the referring veterinarian. It was only fair.

"But you did the work. You should check it!"

"The injuries were straight forward. I expect no complications, so Scotch will do fine with Dr. Melton checking him. If he has any problems, I'll be glad to consult with him, at no charge to you."

"Well...okay, but I'd rather you come back."

"Dr. Melton will take good care of you."

I cleaned up my instruments as Mr. Tyler put Scotch in the barn. He was soon on his way to work.

I did not expect to see Mr. Tyler again, but he and Dr. Melton had a falling out, so he asked me to do his veterinary work full time. Under those circumstances, I agreed.

As I got to know the Tylers I learned that Mr. Tyler and his wife, Rita, purchased three Quarter Horses for their son and daughter, who rode in a drill team. The team practiced several times a week in the summer and had performances on the weekend at various rodeos and horse shows. It was a good activity to keep teenagers out of trouble, but it demanded a huge time commitment on the part of the parents. Like the parents of gymnasts or ice skaters, these parents were devoted to their children. For ten years the Tylers had hauled the horses twice a week to practices or performances throughout the country. However, by the time I met the Tylers, their children were grown and living on their own, leaving Mr. Tyler to care for the horses, which sat idle in their paddocks. The Tylers continued to provide a loving home for the horses, and even attended horse management seminars to learn more.

I had been working for Mr. Tyler for over a year when one day he called me to schedule the horses' spring check-ups. He told me he had lost his job, and between interviews he had a lot of time on his hands, so we could schedule it anytime. I expressed my sympathy about his misfortune, and wished him luck in his job search. He was a hard working man, and I was certain he would be employed again soon. I agreed to come early the following week.

On the scheduled day, I drove to Mr. Tyler's house. I greeted him in the driveway in front of his house. As I prepared my equipment, I asked him how his job search was going.

"Who told you I lost my job!" he asked sharply as he glared at me. I was surprised at his anger, as he had told me about the situation earlier.

Sheepishly, I replied "You did."

"Oh...I guess I did. Well... I'm still looking." He stammered and looked less angry, but now embarrassed.

I guess there'd be no small talk today either.

As soon as I walked into the dry lot I noticed that his horses had gained a lot of weight since my last visit, ballooning into the equine version of couch potatoes. I couldn't call them pasture potatoes, as there was no grass pasture on Mr. Tyler's farm, only dry lots. That meant the horse got so fat from being overfed by Mr. Tyler or his wife, not from the spring flush of grass.

The horses' weights had always been good, and hadn't varied since I began caring for them. I had to gently discover how they got so fat, without raising Mr. Tyler's ire any further.

"Mr. Tyler, I see your boys have put on some weight. If this continues, they might founder. Founder is painful and can make them permanently lame. In severe cases the horses need to be put down. Why'd you change their rations? They were doin' fine."

"Well, I think I'm feeding them better now than I ever did," he boasted. "I went to a seminar at the county fairgrounds about equine nutrition, and learned a lot of things I didn't know."

This should have been a good thing, as most vets agree an educated client is their best asset. But something was amiss.

Quarter Horses are "easy keepers," meaning they don't take many calories to maintain their weight. This serves the horse well in the wild, keeping him alive in times of drought. But it can be a problem for domestic horses, if they are not exercising regularly. And owners tend to give them more feed than they need. But if Mr. Tyler had been to a nutrition seminar, his horses should be looking better, not worse.

"What did you learn?"

"I learned that alfalfa is more nutritious than grass hay."

"That's true."

"I learned that grass hay may be enough for most horses, but adding a little alfalfa to the diet can increase the protein level of the diet and make their coats shinier and their feet healthier."

"That's how I feed my horses." This was going to take some digging.

"I learned that Quarter Horses need about 15 pounds of hay, so I got a scale and weigh their portions now. I still don't give them any oats, as the expert said idle horses don't need it."

All of this information was right, so how did Mr. Tyler's horses get so fat?

After I vaccinated the horses I got out a weight tape, and put it around Scotch's girth to estimate his weight.

"My word, Mr. Tyler! Scotch has gained 115 pounds since I saw him six months ago!"

"I don't think that's possible" declared an astonished Mr. Tyler.

"Well, the tape says otherwise. What are you doin' to make these horses so fat?"

"I'm feeding exactly according to the expert's guidelines. He said Quarter Horses need 15 pounds of hay, so I am giving them 15 pounds for breakfast and 15 pounds for dinner."

Now I understood and I chuckled. "Quarter Horses need 15 pounds of hay per *day*, not per meal. You've been giving them exactly twice their requirement. No wonder they got so heavy!"

"Oh. I thought it was 15 pounds per meal. Come to think of it, I have been going through the hay faster than usual."

Mr. Tyler adjusted their rations and his horses did fine from then on. He was soon employed, and too busy to attend any more seminars.

Chapter 4 Running for Home

Jessie Berger presented her gray gelding, Albert, to me at the finish line of the 50 mile Ride the Range endurance race. The final vet check was the meadow in front of the main barn at Castlewood Arabian Ranch, Betty Carlow's place. Young Jessie was a good rider, and her parents had bought her a tremendously competitive and capable Arabian gelding, well suited to this type of competition. I had vetted the pair in several races previously, and they had always performed well together.

"How was he acting on the trail Jessie?" I asked as I began my exam.

"Dr. Thibeault, he was great! He just wanted to go and go, never tiring."

When I pinched his skin to check for dehydration, it bounced back too slowly, indicating he had been drinking less than he should throughout the day's competition and needed more water to recover from his workout. But all in all, he was in good shape for a horse that just completed 50 miles of competition on steep, mountain trails. The cool October temperatures made dehydration less common than when the races were held in the heat of summer.

His mucous membranes were pink, and when I pressed his gums with my thumb to blanch the blood out, the membranes became pink again quickly, indicating his heart was handling the stress of covering 50 miles in a day. A check of Albert's pulse showed it was also higher than it should be. Either Albert had an injury, or the pain was from his gut. Moving the stethoscope to his abdomen I checked for gut activity. I was alarmed to find his gut sounds were noticeably decreased. While outwardly he looked fine, inwardly Albert was showing signs of stress. If he didn't improve quickly, he could be in serious trouble. Endurance horses that are ridden too hard can shut their gut down. This condition, called ileus, is a form of colic that strikes athletic horses. It can be fatal, so I took my findings seriously.

Albert was more stressed than Jessie thought.

"Tell me what happened since the vet check at Spruce Hill. Your trail card says he passed his exam there in good shape."

Veterinarians examine endurance horses before, during, and after all competitions that are sanctioned by the American Endurance Ride Conference (AERC). During the race, horses are examined every few miles, so the veterinarians can keep a close eye on them and make sure they aren't being ridden too hard. There are also mandatory rest stops, where horses and riders eat and drink, sponge off the sweat, and adjust any tack that might be causing a problem.

"Since Spruce Hill I just asked him for a gentle lope, and I was riding with Brandy and her gelding Topper. We were talking about the hired hand, Ty, who just started working at the ranch. He's so cute, in those tight cowboy-cut jeans. And he can really ride! Anyway, the horses loped along most of the last ten miles, and they seemed to really like it. Of course we slowed down where the trail was rocky, and at the creek crossing. Why? What's wrong?"

"He's not recovering like he should. Let's have Dr. Brown take a look at him."

Luckily there was a second vet checking horses at the finish line. Riders can take it personally when told they've over-ridden their horses. By asking Phil Brown to examine Albert, Jessie wouldn't think I was being unfair to her.

After examining Albert, Dr. Brown concurred. Albert was not recovering from his exercise appropriately.

"You'll have to give her a 15 minute hold."

"Yeah, I know. I just wanted a second opinion. I do some work for her family and I'm sure they won't like it. She'll lose her first place finish."

"They may not like it, but it's your job."

"Yeah, I know. I have to protect Albert. I just wanted to be sure I wasn't over-reacting. I have to be fair to both Jessie and Albert."

You're being fair."

"Thanks, Phil."

I turned back to Jessie and Albert.

"Jessie, his gut sounds are decreased, and his pulse is too high for the post-race standard set by AERC. I have to give you a 15 minute hold. Get some water into him and offer him some lush grass by the creek. If he's only mildly stressed, he'll recover on his own."

"But we were in first place, Dr. Thibeault! That'll drop us to second."

Even though Jessie was a teenager she was already an experienced competitor. Her parents had been leasing an old campaigner from Betty Carlow. Betty's horse, Desert Stormer, had successfully completed a number of 100 mile races, and Jessie had been successful with Storm as he was eased back to 50 mile competitions due to age.

When Jessie's family found Albert, he was a perfect fit. Albert and Jessie had competed in several previous races, and Jessie had always brought Albert home in great shape.

My job as control veterinarian is to speak for the horse. The riders care about the health of their horses, but lack medical training to detect subtle signs that their horses are getting into metabolic trouble. Through seminars and by educating competitors during races, vets can help riders become more observant. Early detection of stress in their horses gives riders the opportunity to avoid serious trouble, rather than relying on treatment to save exhausted horses during competitions.

Endurance riders are often well attuned to lameness because they can see injuries like swollen joints or bleeding, and observe injured horses limping. But endurance horses rarely die of lameness - they die from metabolic problems. The stress of riding a horse beyond its physical ability can cause a cascade of events including heat stroke, dehydration and colic. These problems are always serious, and when they occur out on the trail, miles from help, they can be fatal.

27

As Jessie walked away with Albert I called "Jessie. Do you have electrolytes?"

"Yes."

"Then offer him a bucket of water with electrolytes and a bucket of plain water. Now go find him some grass. Get him back to me in 15 minutes and I'll re-check him. If he won't graze, bring him back right away."

Healthy horses always want to graze, especially when the summer grass is green, and after such a long ride Albert should be hungry, eager to replenish the calories he burned in competition. If Albert's stomach was bothering him so much that he wouldn't graze, I'd know Albert was in serious trouble. I had to monitor him closely, because stressed horses can get worse fast.

"Will he be okay?" Jessie was concerned.

"I think he will, but I'll need to keep a close eye on him. If he gets worse, I'll have to treat him. Go do your job and I'll see you in 15 minutes."

In 15 minutes Jessie and Albert were back.

"How much did he drink?"

"About a half dozen swallows."

"Good. That's a step in the right direction. Did he eat?"

"Only a little. He must not be feeling well, because he just picked at the grass. He ate some, but not with his usual enthusiasm. I thought he was feeling fine at the end of the race. Really Dr. Thibeault, I didn't push him to go fast! He wanted to go on his own. I never would have made him go if I knew he was too tired."

"I know you wouldn't Jessie, and I know you've trained Albert so he's really fit. Because this race was held with your home barn as base camp and Albert knew he was going home, he pushed *himself* too hard. You know how much horses love to go home. That's where the term "barn sour" comes from. He ignored how tired he was and ran back to the barn."

"Honest. I never pushed him! I just let him run at his own pace."

"I believe you, Jessie. You didn't force him - he did it to himself. But it's our job, as veterinarian and rider, to protect the horse, even from himself. I'll teach you how to keep Albert from hurting himself the next time."

I put my stethoscope over Albert's abdomen. His gut sounds were improving, and his pulse was dropping, but it was still not slow enough for completion status according to AERC rules.

"He's better, but his pulse is still not down into the target range. Jessie, I have to disqualify you."

"No!"

A disqualification meant although Jessie and Albert had covered the entire 50 mile course, the record book would show she did not complete a qualified ride because she brought the horse to the finish line in a fatigued state. The rules of endurance racing are designed to prevent horses from being injured. I hoped a disqualification would make Jessie more attuned to her horse's condition in the future, and prevent her from pushing him beyond his limit again. That was the purpose of the AERC rules.

Seeing that Albert wouldn't eat, and seeing my concern, Jessie was beginning to realize that Albert was in serious trouble. Her focus shifted from talking with her friend and getting a prize, to concern for having injured her horse.

"What if he doesn't get better? Does it mean he'll be lame tomorrow?"

I had tried to shield Jessie from fully knowing the severity of Albert's condition until I was certain how bad he was, but I had to answer her direct question honestly.

"No, Jessie. If his gut shuts down completely, it means he could die tonight."

"No! Dr. Thibeault, do something. Please!" Jessie now understood how serious Albert's condition was.

"We are. Letting him rest and replenish himself with water and grass may be all he needs to get better. He's coming around on his own. We'll work together to keep an eye on him and make sure he keeps improving, or we'll treat him with fluids, depending on how the next hour goes. Don't worry. We'll take good care of him. I promise.

"I'm staying to judge the Best Conditioned Horse, and for the awards presentations. Now, get him back to his stall and give him some hay and water. Let him rest there. I'll recheck him in his stall in about 30 minutes. If he acts painful before then, get me right away."

"Okay, Dr. Thibeault."

When I checked Albert in his stall, he was on the road to recovery. His gut sounds were improving, along with his appetite, and his pulse was nearly normal.

As I re-checked Albert I taught Jessie how to monitor his condition by taking his vital signs. She was now eager to learn. And I told her to focus on subtle indications Albert may be giving regarding his willingness to go on. I told her to focus more on him, and less on conversations with her friends. I hoped I had gotten through. Only time would tell.

Later that night, as I was leaving for home, it was clear Albert was going to be okay. Jessie asked me how to care for Albert over the next few days.

"When can I begin riding him again?"

"Give him complete rest for a few days, and then he'll tell you when he's ready. He'll probably need a few days longer than usual to recover from his effort today. When he's eating well, and gallops around the meadow when you turn him out, he'll be ready to ride.

"Okay. Thank you so much, Dr. Thibeault, for helping Albert. I really appreciate it!"

"See you, Jessie. Take care. Albert's gonna be fine. Don't worry."

Albert recovered without medical treatment, but I wondered what Jessie's response would be the next time we met at an endurance race, and if her parents would ever call me again.

It was a tough call, but I had no choice. I had to protect Albert.

Chapter 5 She's a Boy!

I reached into the front seat of my truck, avoiding Clancy's kisses that smudge my sunglasses, while trying to get the book of health certificates and Coggins' Test forms. Angie and Todd Palmer were taking their horses to Wyoming for a trail ride in the Medicine Bow Range. They had scheduled an appointment to draw blood for the Coggins' tests for Equine Infectious Anemia, a fatal blood disorder that is transmitted between horses by biting insects. There is no vaccine to prevent the disease, so most states protect their resident horses by requiring that horses entering the state have a negative blood test for EIA shortly before arrival. This Coggins' test, along with a health certificate and brand inspection, would fulfill state regulations, allowing the horses to travel legally.   Because the Coggins' test takes a few days, I appreciated it when the Palmers called ahead.

On a previous visit I had vaccinated their horses against the common coughs and colds horses so often get when stressed by trailer rides, so they should be ready to go.

I walked into the barn carrying the paperwork and tubes for the blood samples.

"Hey, Doc, how's it goin'?" Todd called out from the corner stall as he curried his palomino stallion, Glint of Gold.

"Couldn't be better, Todd."

"Angie's out gettin' Special. Start with Shiloh. He's in the end stall."

31

I examined the chestnut, Foxtrotter gelding while Todd finished with GG. Shiloh was a fine, well-built horse in good health. He showed no signs of disease. Todd and Angie's horses were all well-mannered, so the examination went quickly. Todd soon came into the stall and held Shiloh's halter. Shiloh stood quietly as I slipped the needle into his jugular vein.

As we finished with Shiloh, Angie came into the barn leading her older mare, Special.

"Hey Angie, so you're taking Special this time?"

"Yeah, Doc. She could use the exercise."

This coal black mare with four white stockings and a broad, white blaze was truly the apple of Angie's eye. She had owned Special since she was a foal, over 20 years. The mare had won many ribbons in the show ring when she was younger, and had produced some outstanding foals. Now, as her age was beginning to show, she was mostly retired, just taking Angie on an occasional trail ride. Four years ago Special was bred, but she did not carry the foal to term. After she lost that pregnancy she no longer came in season regularly. Angie had so hoped for another foal from Special, but without outward signs of heat, it is difficult to know when to breed the mare. Even with repeated examinations, tests, and hormone therapy, Special had been unable to carry a foal to term.

I recalled the excitement in her voice when Angie called me last fall to tell me Special was in heat, and very interested in their stallion, GG. Even though it was past the traditional breeding season, Angie bred the mare that night, and bred her again every two days until the mare went out of season. She wanted another foal from Special so badly, that she would take the precautions necessary to nurture a late season foal.

I prepared Angie and Todd for the likelihood that Special wouldn't carry the foal to term, based on her medical history. Older mares have a hard time producing healthy foals, despite receiving the best of care. Angie was still disappointed a few weeks later when the ultrasound examination revealed that the foal was not developing normally. A follow-up exam revealed Special had lost the pregnancy.

Angie continued to hold out hope, regularly checking the mare for signs of heat. Sadly, the mare never showed signs of heat again, so Angie gave up hope of one last foal from Special, and retired her from breeding.

When I saw Special today, I knew immediately something was wrong. The mare did not have the shiny coat and good muscle tone of the other horses on the farm. She was thin. The muscles were wasting away on her neck and her hips, while her abdomen was distended. But her eyes were still bright. I examined the mare, and could find no obvious problems. I drew blood for her Coggins' test but before I filled out her travel papers I told Angie, "This mare is either pregnant, or she's sick."

"You know she can't be pregnant, and she isn't acting sick - she still eats like a horse! She's just slowed down a bit because of her age. She still dominates the herd out in the pasture."

"I have plenty of horses in my practice that are Special's age, but still have good muscle tone and a shiny coat. She looked much better last fall. Something has happened since then. Have you tried to breed her again?"

"No, she hasn't been in heat since we bred her last fall and we know she lost that foal. And believe me - I keep an eye on her! I turned my yearling colt, Flashpoint, out with her. And he hasn't shown any interest in her."

Angie raised an eyebrow and gave out a hearty laugh.

Once horses reach their late teen years, their heat cycles become less regular, and fertility is reduced even if they are cycling. Even young mares don't cycle during the winter, and mares don't come into heat during pregnancy. But still, I have seen some mares conceive on their first breeding when well into their 20s.

I pointed out her poor muscle tone to Angie and Todd. I knew she wasn't being ridden regularly, so the lack of muscle might have been from lack of exercise. But horses that are turned out maintain good muscle tone if they feel well enough to move around. Special had no lameness problems that would keep her from exercising.

All of her weight was concentrated in her abdomen. If she wasn't pregnant, Special was seriously ill.

Liver disease, parasitism, and low protein diets can cause abdominal bloating. I knew the Palmers dewormed their horses regularly, but we hadn't checked the manure to see if any parasites had become resistant to our treatments. Special didn't have jaundice, a yellowing of the whites of the eyes, commonly seen in liver disease. She had not been exposed to any of the common poisonous plants that cause liver damage in horses. Special lived in a dry lot, eating only hay instead of pasture. Her diet was good and the other horses on the farm ate the same hay and looked healthy. I checked her teeth, and they were okay. I couldn't find any signs of illness. She had to be pregnant.

If she was pregnant, and wasn't being fed extra to provide for the foal, she would take nutrients from her own body to nourish the foal. That would account for the muscle loss, and the muscles were being broken down to supply the foal.

Poor nutrition during pregnancy puts both the mare's and foal's lives at risk, and the problem would be even more serious because of the Special's age. She would need to be strong to carry and deliver her foal.

Angie and Todd were convinced I was over-reacting, standing firm on the belief that her condition was caused by her advancing age. Besides, she was eating well and acting normally.

As I packed up my things, I offered to run a panel of blood tests to check out her health, a fecal exam to check for parasites, and offered to test her for pregnancy. They said they'd think about it. I told them not to delay. Special needed help.

As I drove home I mulled over my conversation with the Palmers. It was my job to speak for my patients - to tell the owners about problems that they can't see. I did that, but I couldn't convince them to let me help Special. I had to find a way to be more persuasive. Why couldn't they see Special had a problem? Was it because they saw her every day, and the body changed gradually?

The next afternoon my answering service said I had a call from Angie. She knew I wouldn't have the Coggins' results yet, and I was concerned about Special, so I called her right back.

"Hi. This is Dr. Thibeault. What's goin' on?"

"Dr. Thibeault, do you remember what you said yesterday about Special, that you thought she might possibly be pregnant?"

"I do. Why?"

"Do you still have Special's blood sample from yesterday?"

"No. I sent it to the lab last night, but I think the lab holds on to the samples for a few days. Why?"

"Well, the horseshoer was just here and his wife said she thought Special was pregnant. Is there any kind of test you can run on her blood to tell if she's pregnant?"

The horseshoer's wife's opinion carried more weight than mine???

"Seems like I said that yesterday..." I said sarcastically.

"Well...yeah...you did," Angie laughed.

I told Angie I'd call the lab and see if they still had the sample, and if they could run hormone levels on it. If so, I'd call her in a few days with results.

The lab still had Special's sample, and there was enough blood to run the tests. But when the test results came back, they weren't much help.

Hormone testing is very accurate when the breeding date is known. The levels of various hormones fluctuate throughout pregnancy, so by measuring the hormone levels and knowing how many days have passed since the mare was bred, it can be determined if the mare is pregnant.

If the blood levels of hormones are above a certain level, at a certain time, the mare is considered to be pregnant. If hormone levels are below another level, the mare is not pregnant, and if they are in between, you don't really know. Of course, Special's hormone levels were in this middle zone - higher than if she wasn't pregnant, but lower than they should be in a healthy pregnancy.

I hate when that happens.

Angie had no idea when this mare could have been bred, or even if she had been bred. It could have been any day since her last ultrasound seven months ago, when we knew for sure she wasn't pregnant. This is where I had to use my judgment and decide how to interpret these findings for the best interests of the mare and possible foal. Special and Flash certainly weren't talking.

I called Angie.

"Angie, this is Dr. Thibeault. I think I have some good news."

"Is she pregnant?"

"Well...I don't know."

"Isn't that why we ran the test?" I could hear the disgust in her voice.

"Yes, but her hormone level falls in that gray area - higher than an open mare, but lower than we see in early pregnancy. We don't have a breeding date, we only know that she has to be less than seven months pregnant. For her health, we must assume she's pregnant. We need to increase her diet right away, and prepare her for foaling. A rectal exam or ultrasound could help us."

Angie refused to let me do a rectal exam or an ultrasound exam, fearing the exam might cause Special to abort. In reality, rectal palpation is quite safe, but if the mare aborts, the veterinarian gets blamed. Angie was already convinced that a rectal exam will cause abortion, so if one occurred, I'd get blamed. With Special's medical history, I didn't press the issue.

I outlined a new diet for Special - more calories, more protein, and minerals to recover her weight and produce a healthy foal. If Special wasn't pregnant, we'd monitor her weight gain to prevent founder. If she didn't gain weight, we'd need to find out why. For now, we'd consider her pregnant.

I kept in touch with Angie as she reported the mare's progress.

Soon Special was beginning to gain weight and look better. Todd was still not convinced the mare was pregnant, and I couldn't be completely sure myself. If she was, she still might not carry the foal to full term, as she had lost her last two foals. But I knew if she was pregnant, she could lose the foal if she wasn't well fed. If Special aborted an otherwise healthy foal due to malnourishment I would have failed my patient.

I so hoped Angie would get her Special foal this time.

One cold, rainy, October day, while I was confined to the house nursing an aching back, I got an early morning page from the Palmers.

I called them back immediately.

"This is Dr. Thibeault."

"This is Angie. Special had a filly last night! Everything seems fine. Can you come out and check them?" Angie could not contain the excitement in her voice.

"Absolutely! I wouldn't miss this for anything."

Despite the fact that I could hardly move, I was excited for Angie and anxious to see the new foal. I agreed to come right away.

Rain is so rare in Colorado that practically no one has rain gear, but cold weather snow gear will do in a pinch, so I bundled my aching back against the cold. I was stiff enough and needed to stay warm. The dampness made the cold go right through me. At least the Palmers had a good barn.

I got to the farm and found no long line of cars in the driveway this time. Special and her foal were in the barn, toweled dry by Angie and Todd. It was dark in the barn on this rainy, gray day, but the Palmers' faces lit up with beaming smiles.

"We've named her Mik."

Todd's strong arms cradled the foal for my exam. This big, bouncing youngster was already quite sturdy on her feet, a sign that she was several hours old. The foal had been born outside, but the Palmers had brought her inside their warm barn and toweled her dry as soon as she was discovered.

Several of my clients had lost newborn foals due to hypothermia when the foals were born outside during chilling fall rains and were not brought into the shelter of a barn. Newborn foals soon deplete their fat reserves by shivering to maintain body temperature. The Palmers quick actions saved their filly's life. The navel had been dunked in disinfectant and Angie had given the foal an enema. They had taken the foal's temperature, and it was a little low, but the foal was warming up with vigorous rubbing and a tiny insulated foal blanket.

I checked the foal's long legs and found no abnormalities. They were long and gangly as expected. I listened to the foal's heart and lungs, which were strong and clear. My back was too sore to look for an umbilical hernia, but my fingers palpated the filly's abdomen and found no problems.

There were no signs of prematurity or ill health, and I assured Angie that Special's foal seemed just fine.

Special looked terrific. The new diet had improved her weight and her winter coat was thick and shiny. Clearly her only problem had been trying to produce a foal on a diet inadequate for pregnancy. Once that problem was corrected, she blossomed into a healthy broodmare. The delivery didn't seem to bother her at all, and she nurtured her foal lovingly. She had plenty of colostrum, and the vaccination program we had followed made sure the colostrum was packed with protective antibodies for the foal.

With the exam over, I followed Angie and Todd to the house to escape the chilling drizzle. We sought the warmth of the house for some hot tea and conversation.

I settled my aching back into one of the easy chairs in front of the fireplace. Todd had a seat at the kitchen counter, and began doodling while Angie fixed the tea. He drew a sketch of his barn, with horses' heads poking out of every stall. He went on to fill the hay loft with stacks of horses lying on their sides, and put a few horses in the feed room and tack room. He drew Angie standing off to the side, hands on her hips, saying "Todd, I think we can fit another one in here." Angie got a chuckle when she saw what he had done.

Angie served the tea and Todd joined us by the fire. The steaming hot brew restarted my internal furnace, bringing me back to life. It was such a good feeling to share the Palmers' joy of Special's healthy foal, after having shared their sorrow at the disappointment of so many lost pregnancies. I advised the Palmers how to increase Special's diet to help her produce milk for the foal. Then Todd recounted the story of finding the filly.

Todd had been convinced that Special was not pregnant. He knew the mare's hormone levels were in the gray zone, and since she had lost her recent foals, he thought she probably would lose this one. He didn't want to get his hopes up.

Todd, a policeman who works the late shift, said he came home from work as the sun was just coming up. Because of the rain and low lying clouds, it was still nearly dark as he fed the horses. Special was in a field with the other horses, but chose not to be near them in the loafing barn that Todd had built just for such weather. Todd noted that she was standing off by herself. This was unusual for Special, who ruled the herd.

"Then I noticed that Special had an extra set of legs." Todd mused.

"My first thought was that one of my neighbor's foals had gotten through the fence, and Special was protecting it from our geldings. Then I remembered that none of the neighbor's mares *had* foals."

"I also noticed the foal looked remarkably like Special."

Todd said he ran into the house, where Angie was still in bed, yelling, "Angie, get out here! *Now!*"

Angie ran outside and led Special while Todd carried the foal into the barn to dry them off. Special was an experienced broodmare and she was comfortable around the Palmers. She let them carry her foal. She enjoyed the attention, and the wool blanket they put on her to stave off the October chill. The barn doors were closed so the horses could warm up. While Angie was toweling the foal's rump, Todd asked what sex the foal was. Angie raised the foal's tail and said "A filly?"

Todd said "That's great. A filly's what you've been hoping for. Then Angie went to the house and called you."

I was so happy they finally had a healthy foal from Special. This filly was a miracle.

By counting back the months, it was apparent Special had been bred right after she lost the previous pregnancy. The Palmer's yearling colt, Flashpoint, had been turned out in the pasture with the geldings and Special - the previously infertile mare. Flashpoint had to be the sire.

I don't know why Special lost her two previous foals, or why she showed almost no signs of heat for four years. But I do know she showed no signs of heat this year because she was in foal.

Todd was in a talkative mood, and after recounting his story he went on to philosophize about his views on horses. Having told me years ago that "horses are born trying to die and it's our job to slow them down," I was eager to hear what he had to say today.

"Hey, Doc. Have you ever thought about zippers?"

I had to admit that I didn't spend much time thinking about zippers.

"What about zippers?"

"Well, if horses had zippers over all of the parts that go bad, you could just unzip them, replace the broken part, and zip 'em back up again."

"Well, that's a great idea! But I don't have a 'used horse parts store' where I can shop. Since you have stallions and mares, why don't you selectively breed your horses to have zippers, and I'll get my colleagues in human medicine, the guys that make artificial hips and things, to work on making spare parts for horses."

Todd had a sly grin on his face as he went on, "And, another thing... about your charges..."

"Yes..." I couldn't wait to hear what was coming next.

"Well, why don't you have two separate sets of fees, one that covers your malpractice insurance, and one that doesn't? You could get people to sign a form that says they won't sue you, and you could charge them less. And for the clients that wanted the right to sue you, you could charge them more, enough to cover the cost of your liability insurance."

"Well Todd, I'll give that some consideration."

Todd's long night shift, combined with the excitement of Special's delivery, had consumed Todd's energy. Sleep was about to overtake him, so I finished my tea and excused myself.

As I got up to go, Angie was telling Todd she might breed Special again next year... Perhaps this was a good time for her to bring it up, as Todd was drifting off.

Two days later Angie called. "Dr. Thibeault, would you believe my new filly is a colt?"

"What???"

"I was watching the foal go to the bathroom in the stall, and she's a boy!"

"What? I thought you told me it was a filly."

"Well, you know since my accident I don't see very well, and I thought she was a filly, but it was dark, and I guess I was mistaken."

I hadn't even checked the sex of the foal, since the Palmers had taken the foal's temperature and given it an enema. When Angie told me it was a filly, I had no reason to doubt her. I forgot that Angie had blurry vision due to a riding accident months before.

Oh well.

Chapter 6 The Bigger They Are, The Harder They Fall

The phone rang. It was Larry Whitley gasping into the phone "Jet is due to have his sutures out this weekend." He coughed. "Can you come on Saturday? I had surgery on my knee, and I'm still on crutches so I called my brother, Leroy, and he can be here Saturday to hold Jet for you."

"Sorry to hear you needed surgery, but I hope it'll help you get back on your bike again soon."

"Yeah, the doc said I can be ridin' again in a few months." Larry wheezed. "I've really missed it, and it sure is hard to get around the horses on crutches."

"I'll bet it is. Yes, Saturday morning at eleven will work for me. How's Jet doing?"

"He seems to be healing up fine. I'll see you then."

Jet was due to be re-checked after his rescue from beneath the barn wall. It was nice of Larry to arrange for someone to hold Jet for me, although the old horse was so gentle, I probably wouldn't need help.

On Saturday morning I drove into Larry's farmyard and Clancy was her usual boisterous self, going into her barking tirade at the sight of Larry's sculptures - barking directly in my right ear.

"Clancy, that'll do. You're deafening me."

I guess she didn't appreciate Larry's rusting tractor art dancing on the wind. I'm not quite sure I got it either. Her instinct took over, deeming that anything that might possibly be alive should be herded into submission.

Clancy stopped barking but continued keeping a wary eye on the seemingly animated creatures.

Larry's pack of mastiffs gushed out from the house as they heard my car approach. They spun like a canine whirlpool behind the fence, jockeying for position near the gate so they could greet me. The dogs had gotten used to me, and now I think they even liked me. I'm not sure if that was an improvement, though, because their greetings were quite boisterous. I was content to stay outside of the yard until the chaos subsided.

I had seen three shiny, new motorcycles in the driveway as I came in and Larry was standing nearby on crutches. He rasped at his dogs to quiet down, his head half hidden by a cloud of smoke from his cigar. Next to him was a man who had to be his brother. The only way to tell them apart was that his brother was covered in tattoos - biker tattoos. His companions were also tattooed, bearded and dressed in black biker leather.

Larry yelled "Quiet!!" at his dogs, and they calmed down momentarily.

"Doc, I'd like you to meet Leroy, my younger brother." Larry sputtered between coughs.

"Nice to meet you, Leroy." I positioned myself upwind of the smoke, and Leroy shook my hand, nearly crushing my puny hand in his. Yow! I know men use a handshake as a test of strength between men, but I never understood why a man would need a show of strength when greeting a woman. I give up already!

Oh well, at least he should be helpful if we needed brute strength, I thought, as I massaged my sore hand, flexing it to see if anything was broken.

"Leroy will help you with Jet today, but I have to warn you - Leroy faints when he sees needles or blood, so don't let him see anything."

Oh, brother!

"Well Larry, there won't be any blood or needles when removing Jet's stitches, but it's time for both horses to get their vaccinations. I'll put Leroy on the other side of Jet, so he can't see anything. That ought to be okay. And besides, Jet will probably stand perfectly still on his own."

"Just be sure he can't see anything!" Larry replied emphatically, as he continued to belch smoke.

"Okay! Okay!"

Larry barked at the dogs again and they sullenly retreated into the house. He then took Leroy to fetch Jet. I followed through the now empty yard.

Leroy's friends followed us to the paddock gate. They were curious about what I was going to do. I find that a veterinary appointment often is the social event of the day in rural communities. It seemed that everyone who had ever owned a horse showed up to express their opinions, but I didn't mind an opinionated crowd observing my every move. I was growing confident in my veterinary skills as I gained experience. But oddly enough, none of Leroy's friends spoke a word.

As Larry handed Jet's lead rope to Leroy, I could see Leroy was uncomfortable around horses, but Jet and Red were so gentle I didn't expect any trouble.

Leroy led Jet out of the makeshift barn to the dry lot and I carefully positioned him on the opposite side from where I was working. Jet's wounds had healed nicely, and even his ear was looking considerably better. As I removed the sutures, Larry hobbled closer to Jet, bringing his smoke cloud with him. When he got a good look at the ear, he commented that Jet's ear looked better than he had expected.

"Maybe that ear will heal well enough that we can consider halter classes again, huh. What do you think, Doc?"

"Yeah, right." Larry had a great sense of humor.

Leroy stood tall for the stitch removal, but as I went back to the truck to fill the syringes with vaccine, Larry hobbled along behind me, dragging his cloud of smoke with him.

"Now I'm serious, Doc. Don't let Leroy catch sight of the needles. He'll faint dead away. I'm not kidding."

"Okay. Okay. I've got everything taken care of. I have a towel on my tray to cover the syringes and I'll keep Leroy on the opposite side where he can't see anything. He'll be fine."

"He won't be fine if he sees anything at all. I'm tellin' ya. He's got a real fear of needles!"

"Well, it's not like *he's* getting the injections. I'm giving them to the horses, for goodness sake!"

"It won't matter. Leroy can't stand the sight of needles. I'm warning you."

It seemed incomprehensible that a grown man, a huge, tattooed grown man, would faint at the sight of a needle.

"How did he get those tattoos if he's so afraid of needles?"

"His buddies helped him down so much alcohol that he was nearly unconscious when he got his tattoos."

"All of them?"

"Yep. Every time."

Good grief!

I carefully re-positioned Leroy on the opposite side of Jet, and cleaned a small spot on Jet's neck with alcohol. Jet was a tall horse, much taller than Leroy, so there was no way Leroy could see anything. I shielded my instrument tray behind Jet's neck in order to block Leroy's view. I removed the towel covering the syringe, pulled the cap off the needle and gently inserted it into Jet's neck. When the needle went through his skin, Jet didn't even flinch, but as I began to inject the vaccine, Jet's head suddenly plunged downward and the old horse staggered and fell to his knees. What the......?

Then I heard the thud, as Leroy hit the ground, face down in the muck, still holding tightly onto Jet's halter. As Larry never mucked out, anywhere Leroy had fallen would have been in the manure, but he landed in a particularly fresh spot. Leroy's formerly silent friends were overcome with boisterous laughter.

Jet quickly leapt to his feet and bolted across the paddock. He wasn't afraid of me, or of the vaccinations, but he was terrified that whatever attacked Leroy might get him next.

The paddock was so small that Jet had nowhere to go to escape the unseen danger. I was afraid Leroy would get stepped on, so I grabbed Jet's lead and hung on as he dragged me to the back fence. Larry was thinking the same thing, but he couldn't move fast enough to grab Jet, so he reached for the paddock gate.

Larry croaked to Leroy's friends, "Get Leroy outta here, 'fore Jet tramples him," as he swung the gate open for them.

Leroy's friends obliged, although they were now petrified of Jet, who was straining at the end of the rope, trying to get away from Leroy. Jet wasn't so sure about them either.

The bikers crashed through the narrow gateway, trying to rescue Leroy before Jet came back that way. Leroy's feet were close to the gate, so they grabbed his ankles and dragged him backwards, face down, through the manure and out the gate.

Jet began to relax once Leroy was gone. Larry limped across the pen to reassure Jet. I handed him the lead rope as soon as Jet was calm enough.

When I looked back at the gate, Leroy and his friends were nowhere to be seen.

"Doc, I *told* you not to let Leroy see the needle! Leroy just can't handle it."

"There is *no way* he saw that needle! Jet's neck was in the way!" I insisted.

"Well, he must have *thought* he saw it."

Oh, brother!

Jet was back to normal, relieved to have a familiar handler at his side.

Larry helped me finish the vaccinations, which went uneventfully in Leroy's absence.

By the time I got back to the truck, Leroy was sitting upright on the front porch. I could tell he was still pale even through his beard and the coating of muck. He was getting some ribbing from his friends. I'd bet a few foamy mugs would be emptied tonight at the local bar, and this story would be retold in biker circles for a long time to come.

As I disposed of the needles and syringes, I made sure to position myself between the tray and Leroy.

Larry came out of the house and his pack followed him to the gate near my truck. Larry gave Clancy her treat and we were soon on our way.

I guess the old saying "The bigger they are, the harder they fall," is true after all.

Jet's wounds healed. Although his legs will forever bear the scars of his ordeal with the barn wall, as luck would have it, his ear healed without a blemish.

Chapter 7 Tequila and Prune Juice

One rainy fall day, I had just settled down by the phone to take calls, when the morning quiet was pierced by the ringing phone. It was Juan Vargas, calling about his black Quarter Horse stallion.

"Dr. Thibeault, this is Juan. Diablo is really sick. He wouldn't eat anything for two days. The stable owner where he is boarded called his own vet to treat him. The vet came out yesterday, but he's still not eating. My friends and I sat up with him all night, but he's not any better. I'm really worried about him. Can you see him today?"

"Yes, Juan, I can. What time works for you?"

"Can you go now? I have to work all day, and if I leave I will get fired. I don't think he can wait until I get off work."

The concern in his voice told me Diablo was in trouble. Juan didn't know who the other vet was, so I had no treatment history.

Juan had moved Diablo to a new place, so he gave me directions and Dr. Mom and I were soon on our way.

I am uncomfortable treating horses after another vet has been there. Pain medications can hide a horse's pain. If I don't know how sick a horse is before treatment, or what drugs were in the horse's system, I'm working in the dark.

But I had no choice. Juan was my client, and Diablo was my patient.

It was a cool day, and Diablo was a stallion who could be fractious. I hoped he would cooperate, because I had no one to restrain him during my exam. Dr. Mom would be riding along, but

47

she'd have to stay in the truck today. I never let her near any horse that might harm her.

I first met Juan and his amigos from the Mexican rodeo when they called me for health certificates and Coggins' tests they needed to trailer their horses to a competition. Since then I had been out several times for a variety of ailments. Juan was my favorite of the bunch though, because he had more common sense than his friends.

As I drove to treat Diablo, I recalled one night, as my family was sharing dinner at a local restaurant, Juan called me to treat one of his friend's horses for colic. He said the horse was down and rolling violently, so I was glad I was nearby.

When I arrived the chestnut gelding, Rojo, was in severe pain, sweating and repeatedly throwing himself down on the hard, gravel driveway. His owner was trying vainly to keep him up.

Juan quickly introduced me to the gelding's owner, Guillermo.

I listened to the Rojo's heart and gut sounds.

"What happened to your horse?"

"I'm so angry!" said Guillermo, "The stupid man that runs this barn doesn't know how to feed horses. He ran out of hay, and instead of getting more hay, he fed the horses full rations of grain instead."

Oh, no! Horses need forages as the staple of their diet. Too much grain would cause gas colic, distending the intestines and stomach painfully.

Rojo's pulse was racing and his intestines were churning non-stop. It had been hours since the horse was fed and his body was digesting the grains, causing the production of excessive gas. Horses have a unique shape to their stomachs, so they can't burp. He couldn't get the pressure off his stomach without help. The gelding kept raising his tail, passing gas, but the intestine is nearly 100 feet long from the mouth to the tail, so he would be sick for a very long time if he had to wait for the gas to be delivered that way.

I gave Rojo pain medication so he would let me pass a stomach tube. Despite his struggles, Guillermo and Juan held him steady while I got the tube down his nose. It was hard to push the tube into his stomach because it was so bloated that the entryway was forced shut. But as soon as I got the tube through, gas belched out of the tube.

When his stomach returned to its normal size the gelding stood more comfortably. His stomach was still churning, and every few seconds more gas came out of the tube He continued to raise his tail. Relieving the pressure would prevent his stomach and intestines from rupturing.

It was now a waiting game. I left the tube in place until the noise subsided.

While we were waiting for the gelding to feel better, I noticed a small mare tied to a flat-bed truck.

"Did someone forget to put that horse away after riding her?" I asked Guillermo.

"No. She lives tied to the truck. The same man that fed my horse rented all of his stalls, so she has no place else to live. She spends all day and night there."

The poor mare had no shade, and the short rope gave her no room to move. The driveway was near a busy road. If she got loose, she could wander out into traffic. If she rested on the gravel driveway, the rocks would damage her skin. I didn't see how she could get up and down without injuring herself under the truck.

When I see horses living like this, I wished the humane laws would allow me to act, but at the time the state regulations on horse care stated that the horse received adequate care if it had food and water. She had food and water, so there was nothing I could do. I had spoken to the owner before, but he wouldn't listen.

When no more gas came out of the tube I coated Rojo's stomach with mineral oil to prevent absorption of any more carbohydrates. I hoped my treatment would prevent laminitis.

"Here's some pain medicine to give him tonight if his pain comes back, but he should be okay. If his pain gets bad again, call me and I'll come right back."

"Thanks, Doc."

I gave Guillermo the drugs and was on my way.

The next time I saw Juan and his buddies, they had moved their horses to another stable. Guillermo's gelding was there, looking fit as a fiddle. Guillermo gave me a grateful smile and a nod as Juan introduced me to another of his friends, Diego, who wanted me to look at a bump on his horse's back.

When I examined Diego's gray stallion, he pointed to a two inch circular lesion centered on top of his spine. The lump was perfectly round, and was about 15 inches behind the withers, right where a rider would sit. It was covered with hair, but was soft - filled with fluid. It looked like a blister. It had to be caused by an ill fitting saddle, but it was in an unusual location. Most saddle sores are on the withers.

"Diego let me see your saddle, please."

Diego reached into his low-rider pick-up and swung the heavy Mexican saddle over the tail gate.

I turned the saddle over, and there was a round leather patch glued to the underside, right on the midline under the cantle. The patch was the same size, same shape, and same location as the bump on the stallion's back. The makeshift repair was obviously the problem.

"There's your problem, Diego. The patch is creating a pressure sore. You need to get the saddle properly repaired by a professional saddler and give your horse time to heal."

"That can't be causing the problem, because I use a thick saddle pad."

I could see this wasn't going to be easy.

"A thick pad doesn't remove the pressure. It's like having a rock in your shoe. Even with thick socks, you can still feel the rock."

"Well, the saddle is *not* the problem. Just fix him so I can ride him. I have a roping exhibition on Sunday."

I tried to hold my temper. Making the connection between the patch and the injury was about as hard as putting a round peg in a round hole. Why couldn't Diego see it?

"The saddle *is* the problem. And I can't fix him overnight. He needs time to heal."

"Well I don't know why I called you anyway, if you can't figure out what's wrong, and you can't fix it."

I took a deep breath.

"I can put some salve on it to take reduce the swelling and soreness, but you must let it heal. If you ride him too soon, and if you don't get your saddle properly repaired, the problem will only get worse."

Diego was not happy. And neither was I.

As I went back to my truck to prepare the salve for Diego's horse, I muttered under my breath, "Even if you don't like the truth, it's still the truth."

I treated the horse's back and left a jar for Diego, but I didn't have much confidence that he would use it.

While it's flattering that clients think I can heal a wound instantly, my honesty disappointments them.

Diego was not likely to become one of my long-term clients.

At least Juan did not harbor such unrealistic expectations.

Driving to Juan's barn took us through a poor part of town. There were yards devoid of grass, with pick-up trucks in the front yards and ramshackle barns behind the small wooden houses. Dogs and children played in the dirt streets. Some of the houses were occupied by my clients, members of the Mexican Rodeo, who had come to Colorado seeking a better life. They brought their love of horses and the vaquero way of life with them. While they often found low paying jobs, somehow they managed to send money back to their families in Mexico. How bad were their lives in Mexico that this was an improvement?

But they loved their horses, and I never saw any neglect. Their horses were well fed and well groomed, and they paid their bills. The stables were clean, but were often on the verge of collapse.

When we arrived at the address, I found Diablo's stable was nothing but a pile of pallets tied together with baling twine. Inside I found Diablo, standing quietly under the blue nylon tarp which had been stretched over the top of the pallets to keep the rain off. The stall was spotlessly clean and deeply bedded in fresh straw.

As I looked around the stall, I saw no manure. Since Juan had gone to work hours earlier, it meant that Diablo's intestines had slowed down or stopped. The top of the straw was level however, indicating that Diablo had not been down on the ground, rolling and thrashing in pain. His water bucket was full to the top, but the water was so discolored it was nearly black. It was hard to see, as there was no electricity or windows in Diablo's stall. The sun was filtered through the rain clouds and the blue tarp ceiling, which cast a bluish tint over everything.

Diablo was so sick that he was as gentle as a lamb. He had no fever, so an infection was ruled out. His pulse was mildly elevated, and the sounds his intestines made were decreased. My findings were pointing to mild pain due to a problem in his intestines.

The hay in his manger was untouched. The other vet's treatment, whatever it had been, had not restored Diablo's appetite. Everything pointed to impaction colic - feed stuck in the intestine, unable to pass through. It was critical that he drink plenty of water to soften the blockage, but this water looked awful. No wonder he wasn't drinking.

Pain relievers would make him feel better. Eating and drinking would get his intestines going again.

I administered a pain reliever and put mineral oil in his stomach to lubricate the impaction. I stayed by his side until Diablo showed improvement. I would call Juan and I hoped to have good news. If my diagnosis was right, Diablo should be back to his feisty self soon enough.

While I waited for the medication to take affect, I cleaned up by the truck. Dr. Mom called to me from the front seat.

"Did you see that?" she said, grinning from ear to ear. She looked like the cat that ate the mouse. I knew something was up.

"What?"

"Look over there." She pointed to the side of Diablo's stall.

Lined up along the side wall were 18 empty tequila bottles and several empty gallon prune juice bottles.

"Juan came to the same diagnosis, but a different treatment."

Now I knew what had discolored the water! I dumped the prune juice-water combination from Diablo's bucket and refilled it with fresh water. Getting water into a horse with an impaction is very important, and Diablo was not quenching his thirst with prune juice.

In about 20 minutes the medications were working, and Diablo began nibbling at his hay. He soon took a few deep swallows of the fresh water. Diablo was on the road to recovery.

We drove out the lane while images of Juan and his amigos, sitting up all night with Diablo, fending off the evening chill with their bottles of tequila, for medicinal purposes only, of course.

Chapter 8 The Day the Ponies Ran Away

As I drove down the bumpy lane I could see the red wooden stable tucked beneath the sheltering limbs of the ancient oak beside the creek. I parked in the farmyard, grabbed my vaccines and walked inside. I was met by the pleasant scents of a clean horse barn - fresh cut hay, sweet pine shavings, and the earthy aroma of horses. The scent always comforted me, like walking out of a winter's storm into a cabin warmed by a crackling, pine fire.

My pony patients, Domino and Brownie, were in their stalls munching hay. Domino stuck his head over the stall door when he saw me coming. His black body was accented with a broad, white blaze and four white stockings. He looked like a diminutive version of a Shire, but the proud way he carried himself expressed how grand he knew he was.

Brownie ignored me, continuing to eat as if it was his last meal. The sun shining through the window made his red coat shine like polished copper. He was gentle and mild mannered, and totally devoted to Domino. He followed him everywhere in the pasture, like a little brother tagging behind.

I loved coming to the Kellys' farm. The young sisters, Kathleen and Molly, were so polite. They were always ready for me, and groomed their ponies to perfection before each appointment. Today I'd come to protect the ponies from sleeping sickness - a disease the summer mosquitoes might bring.

"Dr. Thibeault, thank you so much for coming. Thank you for taking care of our ponies" said Kathleen from the back of Domino's stall, as she finished brushing his tail.

"You're welcome," I said, and I really meant it.

"And please Dr. Thibeault, if you have the time, could you please answer some questions for us? We're writing papers on horse care for school," said Molly as she put aside her brushes.

"I'd be happy to help."

"Are you sure you have time?" said Kathleen.

"I do."

"Oh, thank you so much," said Molly

The ponies bravely took their injections and I answered the girl's questions. I love teaching people about horses, especially eager, youngsters.

I was soon on my way.

The ponies stayed healthy all summer, but in the fall I returned for their dental exams. Since then, the Kellys and their ponies had moved to a new farm nearby.

When I arrived, I saw no girls in the farmyard and no ponies in the stable, but there was a note on the front door. I walked up the stone path knowing something was amiss, but was puzzled to read:

THE PONIES HAVE RUN AWAY

As their old farm was nearby, I drove down the lane to the abandoned red barn, hoping the ponies were there. Ponies always know the way home, and the red barn had been their home for years. Instead I found Mrs. Kelly walking in the paddock beside the barn.

"Dr. Thibeault, I'm so sorry the ponies aren't ready for you, but they were gone when I came out to feed this morning. We've looked all over for them," she told me as she leaned in the truck window. She looked worried.

"Did you check inside the old barn?"

"Yes, that's the first place we went. They're not in the paddock, either. Molly is looking down the lane towards town, and Kathleen is searching along the creek."

A bridle path led to an open meadow nearby with a jumping course. It had lush grass - maybe the ponies were having a snack.

"I'll look in the meadow." I wanted to help.

"Thank you Dr. Thibeault. I'm sorry to make you wait."

"Don't worry about that. I just hope the ponies are okay."

We searched everywhere...but the ponies were gone. I had to go to my next case. I met up with the family.

"I'll be working nearby, so if you find them soon, give me a call and I can come right back."

"Thank you so much, Dr. T."

Off I went, but I worried about the ponies. I hoped they hadn't been stolen. And traffic was dangerous to loose ponies. Ponies shouldn't wander about unattended.

When I stopped for lunch I called Mrs. Kelly, but she had seen no sign of the ponies. So I worried even more the rest of the day. They had been missing a long time - long enough to get into trouble.

By the time I got home it was already dark, and there still was no word. The thought of the young girls looking in vain for their beloved ponies was breaking my heart. What if something bad happened to the ponies?

I was anxious for good news. I had to call.

"Hello. Mrs. Kelly, did you ever find the ponies?"

"No, we never did."

They surely had come to some harm by now, I worried!

"...but at feeding time they trotted down the drive, Domino in the lead, his head held high, and Brownie close behind. They went right into their stalls and put their heads in their empty mangers, nickering for dinner!"

I could hear the joy in her voice. Her daughters' ponies were safe.

"I'm so glad they're home!" I rejoiced.

"So are the girls."

"We'll never know where they went," I admitted, "but I'm sure they had a big adventure, roaming the countryside all day."

"That they did."

The next time I went to the Kellys' farm, I noticed an extra latch on the gate. The ponies would be safe, but they'd have to live their adventures on the farm.

Chapter 9 Floating in The Water Tank

It was summer, and my flower garden was spectacular. The petunias were in full bloom, and the daylilies were gloriously displayed in front of the lilac bushes. I had been enjoying an afternoon working in the garden after attending to a few patients in the morning. When my pager went off, I didn't grumble. My back was aching from dead-heading the roses and I was ready to go to the house for some iced tea anyway. Sitting in my truck on the way to someone's house would rest and rejuvenate me.

The call was from Larry Whitley. He sounded more upset than I had ever heard him before.

"Doc, you won't believe it, but it's Jet again!"

"What's he done this time?"

"He's stuck, upside down, in the water tank!"

"You've got to be kidding!"

"No, but I wish I was!"

I knew that Larry had a water trough in his paddock for the horses, but it was only about six feet long. How on earth could a 16 hand thoroughbred have gotten into the water tank in the first place? And how did he wind up on his back?

I could only envision Jet, on his back with his legs flailing helplessly in the air, looking like a 1200 pound upside-down turtle that needs help getting righted. But there was no room for Jet's long back and neck in the small tank. If Larry said it happened, it must be true, but I had trouble understanding how.

57

"I'll be right there. Is the fire department coming?"

"Yes, they're on their way. And the humane society called. They think I'm responsible - that I put him there!"

"What? Do they think you picked him up and tossed him in the tank?"

"Doc, I don't know what they're thinking, but I don't like it!"

Oh, brother! Now I knew why Larry was so upset.

I filled a large mug with iced tea and grabbed my keys. Clancy knew it was an emergency and she raced me to the garage. As usual she won.

"Get in," I called, as I opened the door. "We're going to see Larry." Clancy loved Larry, as he always gave her a treat. Clancy seemed to know Larry's name, and wagged her tail even faster than usual when I told her where we were going.

I settled into my seat, glad for the rest. In 30 minutes I'd have to be ready to help Jet, if he hadn't drowned. His legs would be scraped from thrashing around inside the metal tank, but hopefully at his age he would be sensible enough not to hurt himself seriously. My yoga instructor introduced me to the idea of conscious rest, so I tried to relax all of my muscles while my mind raced through possible scenarios I had faced that might help me today.

This was a new one for me. A friend's horse had walked across a frozen lake and fallen through the ice. Another friend's horse escaped from its pasture and went to town, walked across a swimming pool cover and fell through, needing to be rescued.

I know cowboys may use the water trough as a swimming hole on a hot summer day. I've seen horses stand with the forelegs in their water trough and paw the water. I've even seen horses dunk their muzzles underwater and blow bubbles, but I've never seen a horse fall into its water tank and get stuck on its back.

I didn't take any special demolition equipment with me this time. I couldn't think of anything that would help me lift a 1200 pound horse anyway. The fire department could extricate Jet. They'd rescued him before. And a team of strong, young firefighters, experienced at dealing with motor vehicle wrecks, surely had the equipment, training and muscle to handle this emergency.

For the humane society to hold Larry responsible for Jet being in the water tank was ridiculous! I tried to imagine Larry, an out-of-shape senior citizen with a bad knee and emphysema, picking up Jet and placing him on his back in the water trough. What *was* the animal control officer thinking?

I was reminded of a nuisance call that came into Horse Helpers one day. Horse Helpers volunteers often act as screening agents for people with complaints about horse neglect and abuse. They answer calls for the Bureau of Animal Protection. The bureau has enough work doing field investigations, so if we screen their calls, they have more time to do their jobs. Some of the complaints we receive are legitimate, so we pass them through, but some are not. Responsible horse owners need to be protected against nonsense complaints from people who know nothing about horses.

Some calls are memorable. People most often call about horses left outside in storms. In my experience, my own horses prefer to be outside in bad weather. Perhaps it's the noise of rain on the roof, or the feeling that they cannot escape by running, but I have observed that even though I leave my barn doors wide open, my horses choose the shelter of the barn only during the worst storms.

If a caller contacted Horse Helpers about a horse left outside in a storm, and the horse was in good health, and in good weight, I assured them the horse will be fine. If the horse was elderly, underweight, or ill, then we would alert the bureau to investigate and educate the owner if necessary about proper horse management.

But one call I'll never forget.

"I want to report a horse in a dangerous situation."

"Okay. I'll see if I can help. What's the problem?"

"My neighbor left her horse outside."

I don't see a problem here.

I began my usual spiel, "The horse should be fine. Horses evolved living outside. Is there grass to eat, and a hill or tree where the horse can seek shelter?"

"Yes, it's a large pasture with plenty of grass, and there are cottonwoods down by the creek, but you don't understand. He's gonna die!"

Obviously, I didn't understand.

"Is the horse thin?"

"No, as a matter of fact it's really fat."

"Then what's the problem?"

"It has shoes on."

I'm still not getting it.

"Horses wear shoes without a problem. Shoes prevent the horse's hooves from wearing down excessively, and corrective shoes actually help with hoof ailments."

I tried to sound reassuring, but the caller was noticeably upset.

"But it's raining!"

I'm still not seeing the problem.

"Ma'am, horses are waterproof. I leave my horses out in the rain all the time. They prefer being outside, getting wet, to standing in a barn and hearing the rain on the roof."

"But he's going to get tetanus!" she said with exasperation.

Now what?

"Horses don't get tetanus from standing in the rain, and most horses are vaccinated against tetanus. The vaccine is very good."

"But, you don't understand!"

Obviously I didn't.

"He's gonna die of tetanus because he has nails in his feet, and the nails will rust!"

Okay... Now I see your problem.

"Ma'am. Horses can wear shoes in the rain. The nails only go through the edge of their hooves, which is dead tissue like the end of our fingernails. Proper shoeing cannot cause tetanus. I assure you, the horse will be okay. My horses have been shod for years, rain or shine, and they're fine."

"Really?"

"Yes. Really!"

Oh, brother!

I was glad to see the Heavy Rescue Unit across from Larry's driveway again as I pulled in. The swaying sculptures were still there also, so Clancy launched into her noisy tirade, barking directly in my right ear. "That'll do, Clancy. That'll do!"

Somehow the firemen had gotten Jet out of the tank, and he was standing in his paddock when I arrived, surrounded by Larry and a crew of rescuers. He looked a little scared, but I think I saw a twinkle in his eye. He had a few scrapes, but nothing requiring sutures or bandages.

After examining Jet I assured Larry he would be okay.

I gave Jet an injection of anti-inflammatory medication. After his ordeal he would be sore tomorrow.

As I was cleaning up, Larry's cordless phone rang. It was the Humane Officer.

Larry was fuming, so he asked me to talk to her.

I assured her Jet was fine and there was no way he wound up in the water tank as a result of neglect or abuse. She took some convincing, but finally agreed not to pursue the matter.

I hung up and told Larry that he should have no more trouble with the Humane Society regarding this incident.

Once the excitement was over, Larry couldn't resist saying "Doc, Jet's ear looks so good, that I think I'm gonna enter him in the halter class at the Stock Show next year. What do you think?"

There are no halter classes for aged thoroughbred geldings at the Stock Show.

"Sure, Larry. He just might have a chance."

I joked with Larry, "But Larry, you've got to find Jet a hobby. The ones he's finding for himself aren't so good."

We both had a good laugh, and Jet didn't seem to mind.

As I climbed into my truck, Larry reached into his pocket for Clancy's treat, and handed it to her through the truck window.

I was on the road with a few hours of daylight left, eager to resume gardening and glad my patient was okay.

Chapter 10 Emergencies

I was on back-up for Dr. Johnson, while she attended a veterinary seminar out of state. Her office paged me. When I returned their call, their receptionist told me, "We have a call from Mr. Richard Filbert from Prairie Corners. He's traveling to a rodeo tomorrow and needs a health certificate. Can you do it?"

Clients seem to sign up for the rodeo and make hotel reservations in advance, but let the health and travel papers wait until the last minute. If Mr. Filbert didn't have a current Coggins' test on his horse, he would not be able to legally travel with him.

Veterinarians often joke about "emergency" health certificates. An experienced colleague of mine has a sign in his back office that says "A lack of planning on your part should not create an emergency on my part." But today it would.

I had agreed to cover calls for my colleague, although that only referred to emergencies, not routine appointments. But my appointment schedule was light enough to fit him in today.

"Yes, I can come out at 4 PM today. If he has a current Coggins,' I can write the health certificate on the spot. If not, it'll take a few days to get the test results back."

"Oh, Mr. Filbert travels all the time, so he has a current Coggins test."

If he travels so much, why didn't he plan ahead, instead of waiting until a few hours before he needed to leave to schedule a health exam?

"Tell him I'll meet him at four."

"Thanks. I'll let Mr. Filbert know you are coming."

Dr. Johnson's practice was centered about 50 miles from mine, so it would be a long drive to Prairie Corners. When treating emergencies, the bills are usually high enough to cover the cost of the travel and time, but for a health certificate I wouldn't break even. However, it was a service to the client and my colleague, and I had time to make the call.

When I arrived promptly on schedule, Mr. Filbert was in the house. I knocked on the door, and he came out.

"You're not Dr. Johnson," he cleverly observed.

"Dr. Johnson is attending a veterinary seminar. I'm filling in for her. I'm Dr. Thibeault. Her office said you needed a health certificate today."

"Do you work for Dr. Johnson in Prairie Corners?"

"No. I own a practice in Mountain View."

"Really. That's a long way from here. You aren't going to charge me extra because you drove so far, are you?"

Oh, brother!

"No. When I cover emergencies for Dr. Johnson, I charge what she charges."

"Well, okay then. My brother Tom Filbert lives in Mountain View. He has Quarter Horses, too. I'm sure you've heard of him."

Of course, I should have guessed that he'd be related to Tom Filbert.

"Yes, I did an insurance exam for him on one of his horses."

"Well, come on back. I have the Coggins' in the pick-up. You can copy the numbers while I catch Whiskey."

While Mr. Filbert caught his horse, I filled out the paperwork. Whiskey's Coggins test was current. When Mr. Filbert returned, I examined the gelding and filled out his health certificate. Mr. Filbert paid me, and I was soon on my way.

The charges did not quite cover the cost of my gas.

A few months later, I was preparing dinner for some friends, over-the-road truckers who stopped for a few hours on their way to California. I was again on call for Dr. Johnson, and this time her office called, saying they had been contacted by Richard Filbert's son, Dick, regarding an emergency with one of Richard's horses. I left my friends to return his call.

"Hello. This is Dr. Thibeault."

"Dad is out of town, and I'm lookin' after his horses while he's gone. The fire department called and said one of his horses is hurt. He's pastured a mile down the road from our house. I need you out here right away."

"What seems to be the problem?"

"I don't know. I haven't seen him."

"Well go down there and see what the problem is. It is a long way for me to drive to Prairie Corners, and I need to know if I have to bring any special supplies."

"I can't get there. My car is dead."

How could he be tending his father's horses when he couldn't even get *to* them? It didn't make any sense, but then again, not much about the Filberts made sense to me.

"You need to come to my house and pick me up and take me down there."

Great! So now I'm the local taxi service!

"Can't you walk, or ride a bike there, or have a neighbor take you?"

"No. It's cold! No one else is around, and I can't walk that far!"

When I was in junior high I walked the mile from my house to the boarding stable to ride every day after school. Being too young to drive, I thought it was great the stable was only a mile away. I guess miles are longer now.

Dr. Johnson entrusted me with the care of her patients, so I went.

I had a foreboding this call wouldn't be straightforward. With the Filberts, nothing went smoothly.

I told my friends I hoped to be home for a late dinner, but I didn't believe it myself. They should eat if I wasn't home in two hours. Unfortunately, they were only in town for a short while, and I wasn't going to see much of them.

It was nearly sundown when I arrived at Richard's house. The weather was turning colder, and the snow from last week's storm was still ten inches deep. Dick climbed into my truck and I drove him to the pasture. Clancy ignored him.

The large field had no horses in sight. I put the truck in four-wheel drive and got half-way down the lane to the shed. I hoped I could get out when it was time to go.

Dick went to get a halter. I could see him struggling with the shed door, and 20 minutes later he came back empty-handed.

"I forgot the key to the tackroom. I tried to get the door off the hinges, but it wouldn't budge."

Good grief!

"There's a halter in the back of my truck. Take it and catch the horse."

Dick took the halter and tromped over the first hill and out of sight. I waited. It was getting colder as the sun, shrouded by the gray winter clouds, sunk lower in the western sky. It was growing dark, and still there was no sign of Dick or any of his father's horses. The field was a quarter section - 160 acres of snow-covered sagebrush and yucca. The terrain was rolling, so the horses could be hiding in any number of ravines.

I slid out of the truck. The deep snow was over the top of my boots. I walked to the crest of the first hill, checking the snow for blood that would lead to the injured horse.

In the next draw, against the gray snowscape, I saw Dick following a herd of horses trotting toward me. He was so inept he hadn't been able to catch any of his father's horses, but at least he had found them and I could do a "trot by" exam. There was no blood visible on any of the horses or on the snow after they passed. They all looked fine - trotting soundly.

Breathless and irritated Dick told me "None of my dad's horses are hurt. The fire department was mistaken."

Dick tossed the halter in the back of my truck and climbed in. I drove him back to his house.

I asked Dick if I could use his phone to call the fire department to verify the address and see if we could locate the injured horse. There was an injured horse somewhere nearby, but not in Dick's herd.

"You're so greedy. You just want to get paid for treating this horse, wherever it is, don't you!"

The hackles went up on the back of my neck.

"No, Dick. As a matter of fact, I have friends visiting me tonight, and I'd rather be home with them. My concern is for the horse. It's getting dark and there's an injured horse out there somewhere that needs help! Firemen don't over-react."

I was getting irritated.

I called the dispatcher and assured her that Mr. Filbert's horses were fine. She connected me with the fireman who reported the incident, and he was adamant that the injured horse was at the pasture we had just searched.

"Well, I couldn't find any hurt horses there. I guess that's all I can do."

If there was no place else to look, I might as well go home.

I presented Dick with a bill for my services.

"I'm not authorized to pay this."

"What do you mean? You were authorized to seek medical attention."

"Dad authorized me to get medical help in case of an emergency, but not to pay the bill. So I'm not paying it. You'll have to talk to dad when he gets back in town. And besides, you didn't do anything. The horses are fine, so we don't owe you anything."

I was fuming! I'd had about enough of the Filbert mentality!

"I told you to verify the problem before having me come 50 miles, but you chose to have me come without being certain you needed it. You requested my services. We have a verbal contract. You owe me for my time!"

"Well, I'm not paying you. You'll have to talk to my dad."

I stormed out. I had spent all afternoon and would drive 100 miles before I was home, all at his request, giving up time with my friends, and now he expected my services to be free!

I contacted Richard when he returned. He told me he was not paying the bill because his horse was fine and it wasn't his son's responsibility to check the fireman's report. He told me to send the bill to the fire department.

Certain character traits ran deep in the Filbert family.

Chapter 11 Ten Minutes to Live

One cold January day, Dr. Mom and I were traveling home on the interstate from a thankfully short day of appointments. We were discussing our gardening plans for the coming spring. It had been snowing for days, and the snow was deep. When the snowplows cleared the lanes on the highway, there were mountains of snow on each shoulder. It was like driving down a narrow mountain canyon.

As we neared the turnoff for Mountain View, I spotted a Border collie, trotting anxiously down the shoulder, trying in desperation to get off the road as the cars flew by her. She panicked, tried to scale the steep, snowy walls, but she slid back onto the roadway. Her life expectancy at that moment could be measured in minutes. I would be devastated if she got struck right in front of me.

I rarely pull over for stray dogs because my past experiences have shown that they usually run away from me, and parking on the highway risks my life and the lives of those with me. But I had to break my own rule. I had to stop. It was a Border collie. I envisioned how scared Clancy would be in this situation. I knew the stray might be wary of strangers, but I hoped I could convince her to come to me.

Thankfully the traffic was light, but the cars were flying past. The speed limit on this road was 70 miles per hour, but drivers rarely went that slowly. The piles of snow left no room to get my truck clear of the traffic. As I pulled over, I saw another dog - a Springer spaniel was also loose on the roadway.

I was ruled by my heart and not my head. My truck was already full. Dr. Mom, Clancy and I sat in the three bucket seats, and my x-ray equipment was on the floor in front of Clancy's seat. The rest of the truck was filled with vet supplies in a large wooden chest. There was really no room for one more dog, much less two.

Besides the space issue, what would happen if these two dogs did not get along with each other, or with Clancy, in such cramped quarters? A dogfight inside the truck at highway speeds could spell disaster.

What was I thinking…?

Only that I could not leave this dog on the highway!

Dr. Mom put Clancy on her lap, to make room on Clancy's seat for the other dogs.

The Border collie was frightened and continued running down the road away from me as I pulled over, but the Springer was friendly and came to me quickly. He wagged his tail, eager to get in the truck. When he jumped in, the Border collie stopped, turned around and looked back. She clearly did not want to leave her friend, but her fear of me was strong.

I squatted down to look less intimidating, and called to her. I could tell she was in a dilemma, wanting to go with the other dog, yet afraid of me.

Luckily the Spaniel was barking loudly in the truck, and his pull was too strong. The black and white dog approached me. I remained low and still until she got close. I could see she was wearing a bright pink collar. She was too big-boned and heavy to be a purebred, but she had Border collie traits.

We made eye contact and I could see the fear in her eyes. She wanted to be with her friend, but she was so afraid of me. She had that beautiful, strong eye that Border collies use to control a flock of sheep, and I was sure she would have a good disposition.

"Come on girl,' I whispered. "Going home with me is a good thing. I'll take care of you. Come on."

Her look softened, and I knew I could get her. I gently brought my hand up under her neck and grabbed her collar.

A deep growl rumbled in her throat. Oh brother! Could I hold her without being bitten?

70

For her sake, I was afraid to let her go. I'd never catch her again and she would surely be killed. For my sake, I was afraid to hang on. Was I about to be attacked by the dog I was trying to rescue? She certainly was big enough to do me harm, but the look in her eye told me that she really didn't mean to hurt me, she was just scared.

At least I *hoped* that's what she was thinking.

My safety as a veterinarian depended on being able to read an animal's intentions from its body language, and do it quickly. This was especially important with my equine patients, as they are powerful enough to inflict serious injury or death. If an animal was fearful, I had to reassure it. But, if the animal was aggressive, I had to prevent it from getting the upper hand. If I guessed wrong, I'd pay the consequences. Luckily, I guessed right most of the time.

I overcame my hesitation and picked up the dog, putting her in the back seat. I quickly closed the door behind her, before she could turn around to jump out or bite me in the face. I wasn't far from home, and I could put the strays in the barn while I sorted things out. I just hoped I could get there before a fight broke out.

I ran around to the driver's door and got in. Two soaking wet, strange dogs, two people and one territorial Border collie who had just had her space invaded could be the recipe for a wreck on the highway.

Clancy was curious about the new dogs that took her seat, but not aggressive. The Springer was trying to join Clancy in Dr. Mom's lap in the front seat. At least he was friendly, although his attempts to put his 50 pound frame in her lap, which already held Clancy's 35 pounds, were a bit distracting while I was trying to drive home safely. Meanwhile, the Border collie in the back seat was trying to jump through the closed rear window.

I hurried home and drove straight to the barn. I put the dogs in one of the horse stalls. The Springer had a collar with the name Montana, and a phone number on it, but the collie's collar had no identification. At least one owner was going to be easy to contact. Maybe the same person owned both dogs. The number was local, so the owner would live nearby. I closed the stall door and then let Clancy out in the farmyard. She was so happy the other dogs were locked up and she was free. She gloated at being top dog. Dr. Mom and I went to the house to dry off and call the owner.

While Mom fixed some hot cider I called the Springer's owner. The owner's wife answered, saying that her husband had been out searching for his dog, and she was glad to hear that Montana was safe. She would send him over as soon as he returned. She didn't know who owned the Border collie. The dogs must have paired up after Montana got out.

The owner soon came to retrieve his dog. As it would turn out, Montana became a regular at my farm. He lived in his owner's garage, and when his owner would come home from work and raise the garage door, the dog would bolt out and disappear. I guess Montana liked my house better, and it seemed to be his destination of choice. I suggested obedience school, or fencing a yard for Montana to keep him out of danger, but his owner never did. He only cared enough about Montana to put his phone number on the collar, not to keep the dog safe at home.

Having waved goodbye to Montana and his owner, I called Animal Control. There had been no inquiries about a missing Border collie, but they were willing to shelter her and try to locate her owner.

After feeding my horses, Dr. Mom and I took the dog to the shelter. Much to Clancy's disgust, I left her home. With only one dog in the truck, the drive was a much less chaotic. The collie was beginning to relax, and soon climbed into Dr. Mom's lap. She weighed 60 pounds, so she was more than a lapful, but by the time we got to the shelter she was lying on her back, comfortably sprawled out across Dr. Mom's lap and the entire front seat of the truck. She was completely relaxed while Dr. Mom scratched her stomach. I thought she was a super dog. I hoped she had a caring owner who missed her.

After I parked on the shelter's lot, she begrudgingly managed to rouse herself and walk to the front door.

The Animal Control Officer, whose name tag read 'Diane,' recognized her.

"Oh, it's Boo."

Boo wagged the rear half of her body when she saw a familiar face.

"I thought it might be Boo. She's been here before. We adopted her out to a lady in Mountain View. I'll call her and see what the story is. How ya' doin' Boo?"

She reached down and patted Boo.

"If the owner doesn't claim her, will you call me?"

I can't believe those words came out of *my* mouth.

I already had a dog, and horses, and a growing veterinary practice and a farm to run. What was I saying?! Clearly my heart was still in control over-ruling my brain.

Diane said she'd let me know.

When I got back into the truck I told Dr. Mom that the humane officer knew her, and her name was "Boo." I told her that she had been at the shelter before, and had a new owner. When I told her that I had offered to take her if the owner didn't, Dr. Mom shot me a look like I was crazy.

"I know! I know! I don't need another dog, but she needs a good home - one that won't let her run on the interstate. Besides, she would be great on our farm, or one of my clients would like her. I can't just walk away from her."

"I know. That's why you're a vet, because you care so much about animals. I know you'll make something work for her. But did you see how much hair she has? She must be half Samoyed!"

"Yeah, I know, but what's a little dog hair when you're saving a life?"

A few days later Diane called. She reported that the person who adopted Boo previously did not want her back. Apparently she put Boo on a chain in the backyard, deprived of all human and animal companionship.

That was a tragic choice for Boo. Dogs are social animals. Wild dogs live in packs, and domestic dogs readily bond to other dogs or to humans. Living alone, with no exercise, is unnatural.

Boo begged to get released from her chain by barking. The owner didn't tolerate the barking so she came out of the house and beat Boo. In response to being beaten, Boo bit her, so the owner unsnapped the chain and turned Boo loose.

No wonder Boo had bonded so quickly to Montana. She had been deprived of companionship. And no wonder she had growled at me, as I was probably the next human she encountered after her abusive owner. She must have been overjoyed at being in Dr. Mom's lap, having found the love and companionship she craved.

When I got to the shelter, Diane told me Boo had already been spayed and vaccinated before her last adoption. She gave me Boo's medical records - and a bill for adopting her. Is it crazy to pay an adoption fee for a dog that I could have kept for free a few days ago? Trying to return Boo to her owner - her neglectful, abusive owner - cost me $100!

Oh well. The money goes to a good cause.

Boo was happy to see me. I guess she now recognized me as someone who wouldn't harm her. Today she trotted happily to the truck and jumped right in. She was soon licking Dr. Mom's face, elated to see her again.

I drove Boo to Dr. Paige Garnett's clinic for an exam. Paige was a classmate of mine in vet school, and went into small animal practice after graduation. Even though we received equal training in all species, our interests diverged and we developed our skills along different lines. Consequently, we referred clients to each other as necessary. I have tremendous respect for her skills as a veterinarian and for her honesty as she was one of the rare students who would admit not knowing an answer, rather than trying to dazzle the professor with fancy footwork.

My clients always give me a hard time when they find that I take my dog to a vet, and don't do the work myself. I explain that veterinary medicine is so diverse. A veterinarian who practices on only one species is the equivalent to a human physician who is a general practitioner. To stay current on new developments in equine medicine takes all of my free time. I can't possibly stay current on canine medicine as well as a vet who practices only on companion animals. I tell my clients, "I'm a good horse vet, but not a good dog vet. My dogs deserve to be treated by a good dog vet."

When I led Boo into the exam room, Paige asked me "Well, what are you doing with this new dog, Marcia?"

"She stole my heart. What could I do?"

I told Paige how Boo came into my life.

"Well, let's get her checked out."

The exam went quickly. Boo was in very good health, and young, but because she had been in the shelter, Paige suggested that I treat her for Giardia, an intestinal parasite which is quite contagious between dogs and from dogs to humans.

"We don't want Clancy or your family to get sick. Treat her for two weeks, and pick up after her each time she goes to the bathroom for the next 30 days."

I was quickly on my way, looking forward with great anticipation to walking my new dog on a leash several times a day, in the middle of winter with a pooper-scooper at the ready.

Love is a crazy thing.

Boo got through the 30 days with no signs of illness. If she ever had Giardia, it never spread to Clancy.

Boo could now run free in my farmyard, as it was fenced off from the road. She loved her freedom and the companionship, and seemed to thrive. She did not have Clancy's strong herding instinct, but soon became comfortable around the horses. While Clancy preferred to stay in the paddocks guarding the horses, Boo stayed by my side, so closely that avoiding tripping over her was a challenge. Things were going along quite well except for one problem. In Boo's mind, her life would be perfect if only she could kill Clancy and have me all to herself.

Every time she and Clancy were in close quarters, Boo would growl and scare Clancy so badly that Clancy began avoiding some rooms in the house. I felt so sorry for Clancy, being terrorized in her own home. I tried everything I could think of, and consulted an experienced dog trainer for whom I have great respect. Nothing worked. Boo was going to need to find another home where she could be an only dog, or she had to become socialized.

I contacted a number of my clients and soon found a good option. Betty Carlow ran a boarding stable, Castlewood Arabian Ranch, where she bred, trained and boarded endurance horses. Betty told me that she had recently hired a young wrangler. His name was Ty, and he was looking for a dog.

Ty came to Colorado from Nebraska. It was the first time he had been away from his family. He had left his family dog behind, and missed her dearly. Ty lived in a small cabin on the back of Betty's ranch. I knew that Boo would love sharing a cabin with him.

Betty located her ranch on a tract of land that adjoined a large national forest, so she had access to many miles of beautiful trails in the Rocky Mountains where she conditioned her endurance horses. The ranch was in a gorgeous setting - huge, red rocks poking holes in the horizon, and evergreen forests contrasting against the blue sky. Betty rode deep into the mountains everyday, with her standard poodle and two whippets accompanying her on the trail.

In addition, Betty's boarders also took long training rides to prepare their horses for 50 mile and 100 mile competitions, and they brought their dogs along as well. When I did veterinary work at the ranch I would usually see a herd of horses and a pack of dogs heading out. Betty assured me that her dogs would accept Boo, although I wasn't sure how Boo would accept them.

I soon took Boo to Castlewood.

Betty's ranch was even more beautiful than I had remembered. It was early spring, and the grass was just coming to life. The pale green grass, the deep green forest, and the contrast of the stark red stone thrust against the afternoon clouds was stunning. Castlewood was a small pocket of paradise.

Betty greeted me in the farmyard, her dogs at her side. Boo stuck her head out the truck window, eager to get attention from a stranger.

"So this is Boo. She's beautiful!" Betty said as she ran her fingers through Boo's thick coat. Betty loved animals and welcomed them to her ranch. "Let her out."

Betty's dogs where already surrounding the car, and I didn't want to get into the middle of a dogfight if Boo treated them like she did Clancy.

"I'd rather let her meet Ty one-on-one than subject her to your pack, if you don't mind."

"Sure. I'll put the dogs in the tackroom and we'll go up to Ty's cabin. I think he just finished chores and I know he's anxious to meet her. Come on, dogs."

The pack obediently followed her to the barn. I let Boo out of the truck, and Betty and I walked up the lane toward the cabin. Tan and lean, the young cowboy on the porch pushed his straw hat back on his head as came down the steps to greet us with a wide smile.

"Ohhhh, what a pretty girl! Hi Boo. How are you?" he cooed.

Boo greeted Ty enthusiastically and it was obvious he loved dogs. She was now more trusting of humans and she contentedly sat on his foot, leaning against his shin so he could rub her chest while she stared passively into his eyes."

Betty introduced me to Ty. I didn't introduce Boo to him.

"It doesn't look like you two need any introductions."

"Nope. I think we're hittin' it jus' fine."

We went into the cabin and discussed Boo's history over some lemonade. I stressed to both Betty and Ty that Boo might be aggressive towards other dogs. While we talked Boo stayed at Ty's side. He never took his hands off her.

"Please keep an eye on her. I would feel awful if anyone or any dog was injured by her. She's big enough to do serious damage."

"Don't be so nervous. We get new dogs in here all the time, and they do fine. She'll love it here."

I trusted Betty. She knew her dogs.

Boo had a chance at a great life with Ty, if she didn't blow it.

In a few days I called Ty to see how Boo was doing.

"Ty, this is Dr. Thibeault, calling to see how you're getting along with Boo."

"Oh, Dr. Thibeault, she's great! I just love her! She stays right by my side when I am doing chores, and follows me all around the ranch, although occasionally I trip over her."

"I know what you mean." I replied honestly.

"Shelly, one of our boarders, nicknamed her 'Velcro dog' because she sticks so close to me!"

"That's great!"

"She sleeps right at my feet when I'm in the cabin, and stays next to my bed all night long."

It was comforting to know that Boo had the companionship she craved and rewarded people with such loyalty when allowed to be with them.

"How is she getting along with the other dogs?"

"Well, you know, we have lots of dogs here, and she had to find her place in the pack. At first Boo thought she was gonna be top dog. But some of the other dogs didn't agree. There's been some growling and a nip or two, but nobody's drawn blood. Sometimes Boo will be missing for a couple of hours, but she always comes back. I think she's just hiding in the woods while she figures things out. The ranch is big enough that she can go off alone for a while and still be safe."

"Today I took her on the trail with Betty and John's three dogs and she got along okay. She's doing fine."

"Thanks, Ty, for helping me with Boo. I think she's learning some valuable lessons with you."

"Thank you, for giving me such a great dog!"

As I hung up, I was glad I had stopped that day on the snowy highway. It seems we had a win-win situation, companionship for Ty and a wonderful life for Boo.

Chapter 12 The Horse Trainer

As I settled down to breakfast, the phone rang.

"Hello, Dr. Thibeault? It's Jamie Steele."

"Hi, Jamie. What's up?"

"Remember my new mare, Mystery? Well, she's pestering my old mare, not letting her eat. Tequila is too old to be running around so much. She's losing weight and I'm afraid her arthritis will get worse because Mystery's chasing her. I'm really worried. Can you come out?"

The old mare was the apple of Jamie's eye. I'd be right out.

While driving I remembered how Jamie acquired Mystery.

Jamie loved her Morgan mare, Tequila Sunrise. She had owned the chestnut for nearly twenty years, but Jamie spent years in college pursuing a law degree, so she couldn't afford to breed Tequila until recently. Now the mare was too old to have a foal.

We tried to find out why she wouldn't conceive. I analyzed the mare's hormone levels, and biopsied her womb. The tests came back normal, but the mare would lose the pregnancy after a few weeks. Years of trying yielded no foal. Jamie left the mare in a field with the stallion for a year, letting nature run its course, but Tequila would not stay pregnant. I finally convinced Jamie to take advantage of the newest technology, embryo transfer.

During embryo transfer an egg from Tequila would be fertilized during a natural breeding. The fertilized egg would then be flushed out and put into the womb of a young healthy mare. The recipient mare would carry the foal until its delivery date and then nurse it as her own. There was little risk to either mare, but no one could predict how much longer Tequila would continue producing healthy eggs. Jamie needed to act soon, if she was going to have a foal out of Tequila.

We sent Tequila to the university for the procedure. They keep a herd of mares ready to receive the embryos. The mares are purchased at auction so not much is known about their backgrounds. They are in good health, and well-cared for by the University, but many are young and have never been ridden. Jamie was required to buy the mare that would carry Tequila's foal, but would have no say in selecting the mare. The university would choose a mare at the right stage in her reproductive cycle. They chose an Appaloosa mare that Jamie would later name Mystery.

Jamie and her husband, Tom, built a beautiful two stall barn to house Tequila and the foal she hoped to have someday. Now the second stall was occupied by Mystery, and the Appaloosa mare clearly did not like Tequila. Jamie desperately wanted her old mare to rule the roost, but Mystery was younger, faster, and more agile, and soon pushed Tequila out. Jamie wanted the horses to be together during the day and in their stalls at night, but she was worried about the mares fighting while she was gone to work. She would be devastated if Tequila was injured.

As I pulled into the driveway, I could see Jamie and Tom in the paddock. Before he met Jaime, Tom had no prior experience with horses, but he was willing to help with chores. Tom was bright and had recently graduated from college, but he was clearly out of his element on the farm.

Neither Tom nor Jamie seemed to have a sense of humor - they were always so thoughtful and serious. Normally Jamie's dark brown hair was pulled tightly back into a bun, and her wire-rimmed glasses made her look like an old maid, although she was neither old nor single. She would hurry home from work for Tequila's appointment, still clad in a sweater and skirt, but sporting manure encrusted rubber barn boots. It made an interesting fashion statement.

Today was Saturday so Jamie let her hair down and wore jeans.

"Hello Jamie. Hi Tom. How's it going?

"Not so good. Mystery keeps bullying Tequila, so we put Mystery in the barn," Jamie pouted.

I entered the dusty paddock and joined Jamie under the large cottonwood tree in the corner. Its dense canopy of leaves provided welcome relief from the sun's heat. Tequila joined us in the shade. Her sagging muscles and graying coat signaled her advancing years, but she was eager to check us for treats.

Mystery was locked in the barn, and was not particularly happy it. Rather than munching on her manger full of hay, she stuck her head over the bottom Dutch door and observed our conversation. She looked bored and wanted her freedom, demanding our attention by kicking at the stall door. I ignored her, but Tom yelled at her and she stopped momentarily.

I examined Tequila and could see that she was okay. She had only a few minor bite marks. She had lost some weight, but had been overweight to begin with, so no harm had been done.

"When did you get Mystery home from the college?"

"Two weeks ago."

"Are they getting along any better now than when she first came?"

It is common for horses to show aggression when a new horse enters their territory, but they soon settle their differences and bond to each other. I had seen this with my own horses. But then, I had geldings. Mares could be more difficult. The herd leader is usually a dominant mare, so the situation could be dangerous for Tequila. If Jamie had a large pasture, Tequila could escape Mystery's wrath. In time, they might be able to work things out. But Mystery treated Jamie's entire farm as her personal space.

"No. I think things are worse. Mystery picks on Tequila, and she's getting more aggressive all the time. Tequila hardly gets to eat at all. Mystery drives her away from the feeder. Mystery kicks and squeals and even scares me! I'm sure Tequila is petrified! She's lost weight, and I'm afraid she'll get hurt. I used to leave the barn doors open during the day when I went to work, so they could get outta the weather, but I keep 'em closed now."

"One day I saw Mystery trap Tequila in the stall and I heard them squealing. I know Mystery was kicking at Tequila. I thought she was going to kill her! This has gotta stop."

Mystery again kicked the door. Tom yelled at her to stop.

This situation, two horses sharing less than one acre of dry lot with no grass, was not a good arrangement for two quarreling mares. Being in her 20s, Tequila's need to run for her life on arthritic joints was making her sore. I knew Jamie would be devastated if anything happened to Tequila.

Twice I had destroyed horses who sustained broken legs from being kicked by an aggressive mare. I wanted to prevent that from happening again. We had to do something - now.

"You have no choice. You have to separate them."

Mystery continued kicking the door. Again Tom rushed at her, now flailing his arms in her face, yelling at her to stop. Each time he came, she stopped momentarily. Mystery was enjoying this game. If she couldn't get everyone's attention, at least she had one playmate who came when she kicked.

Jamie whined, "But I want the foal to know her real mom. And I want Tequila to be the boss. I built the barn for *her*!"

"I know that's what you want, but horses have their own social structure within the herd, even if the herd is only two animals. You don't want to risk Tequila's health. After the foal is weaned, you can sell Mystery, and then you'll have what you want, Tequila and her foal in your beautiful new barn, just like you planned."

We now had to raise our voices, as the noise from Mystery's kicking and Tom's yelling had intensified. Mystery was banging on the door in earnest, and got a more animated response from Tom each time. Tom was getting irritated. He was not getting the desired effect - getting the mare to stop kicking the new barn door he had just built.

Every day I have the opportunity to observe horse and human behavior. I enjoy watching people interact with their horses. Humans have been training horses for centuries, and knowledgeable horsemen can look into the horse's mind with clear understanding.

However, most of my clients are professionals in other fields, and their horses are a hobby. They don't devote much time to observing horses, although they may read books and watch videos, or take a riding lesson or two. In these situations, the horse often holds the upper hand, although the client isn't aware of it. And most owners underestimate the intelligence of their horses.

Mystery clearly loved this game, getting Tom to come to her every time she banged the stall door.

I tried to ignore their antics and focus on Jamie's problem.

"If you build a fence on a diagonal from between the stall doors to the corner under that tree, both mares'll have room to exercise, shade, access to water and shelter in the barn from a storm that might come up while you are at work. You'll need a stout fence, with a strand of electric wire at the top to keep the mares from fighting over the fence or getting tangled in it. It's gotta be safe for the foal, because you'll need to keep them separated after the foal is born. You can expect Mystery to be even more aggressive when she has a foal to protect.

"That's your best option. You have to protect them both."

Mystery continued kicking the door. In anger, Tom rushed up and kicked the barn door.

The picture was so comical. I try not to laugh at my clients, but I completely lost control and burst out laughing.

"What's so funny?" asked Tom, with a puzzled look on his face.

I tried to compose myself and replied, "Mystery was bored, and wanted attention, so she banged on the door. You dutifully complied with her wishes, visiting her every time she called you. You wanted to get Mystery to *stop* kicking the door, but instead, she not only trained you to come when she called, she even trained you to kick the door *for* her!"

A smile crept slowly across Tom's face, replacing the puzzled look. "By George, she did do that, didn't she?"

Mystery gave Tom a new meaning for the term "horse trainer."

I bid Jamie and Tom goodbye, and was soon on my way, chuckling all the way home about Mystery's ability to train Tom.

Jamie and Tom built the fence, and soon harmony was restored on the farm. The mares would stand along the fence, enjoying each other's company, as long as neither mare invaded the other's space. Mystery no longer needed to defend her food, and in the spring she delivered a healthy chestnut filly, that was the spitting image of Tequila. Mystery was an excellent mother, and the foal thrived.

The separation suited both horses well. Tequila was able to eat in peace, and regained her lost weight and feisty attitude.

Jamie grew attached to Mystery, thankful for the beautiful, healthy foal she produced. She and Tom gave the mare a loving home.

Chapter 13 The Dangerous Vaccine

Angie and Todd Palmer were some of my favorite clients. They were blessed with common sense, which I find to be such a rare trait I consider the term an oxymoron. They also shared an engaging sense of humor. I enjoyed sitting in their kitchen, after tending to their animals, discussing the issues of the day.

While Angie wanted me to do all of the farm's veterinary work, Todd wanted to save a few dollars and handle the routine work, like vaccinations and dewormings, on their own. I let clients do as much of their own work as they can if they know what they're doing, but I won't let animals suffer needlessly because an unskilled owner is foolishly trying to save money.

Horses like Apache, the paint colt in California, suffered because his owner didn't administer an injection properly. Apache was my first case of owner incompetence, but he was not the last. The cost for Apache's emergency visit far outweighed the money Maureen saved by trying to do her own vet work. If his suffering wasn't enough to change Maureen's mind about when she should seek professional help, I hoped my fees made her think twice.

If Angie chose to do her own work, I'd help her do it well. Because of Apache, I'd devised a plan to help owners do some of their vet work without harming their horses.

By asking my clients about illnesses, vaccines, parasites and dewormers, I assess their level of expertise, and then help them maximize their skills. The language they use reveals how much they can handle.

Some clients openly discuss their abilities and limitations, while others just wait until they get in over their heads and then call for help. As in human medicine, early diagnosis and treatment shortens the recovery time and cost of treatment, but prevention is the best medicine of all.

My goal is to keep my patients in the best possible condition and that's becoming easier with the advances being made in veterinary medicine. The Palmers were balancing the transition to let me do some of their routine work, and handling what they could by themselves. Thankfully they let me determine what they could safely do.

Because Mik was so special, Angie relied on me to handle all of his post-natal care, including vaccinations. I outlined a diet and exercise program for him, protecting his spindly legs from the deformities foals have if the minerals in their diets are not properly balanced. I vaccinated and dewormed Mik on schedule, and he was thriving, sprouting bigger and stronger at every visit.

On the day I was to give Mik his final boosters, Angie opened the gate for me, but she looked worried.

"Good morning, Dr. Thibeault."

"Good morning, Angie. What's wrong?"

"I'm really worried about Mik. My neighbor, Ann Chatfield, called me last night and told me her colt is sick with distemper, and he has it really bad."

I had seen many cases of distemper, and they were rarely mild, so Angie had cause for concern. Distemper was deadly enough to have taken the lives of some of my patients. At Mik's age, he could become seriously ill or die.

The disease is caused by a bacterium, Strep equi, which is similar to the germ that causes strep throat in people. It is highly contagious between horses and spreads rapidly throughout a farm once it gains a foothold. When horses get infected, the lymph nodes under the jaw swell up to the size of a baseball. These swollen glands make swallowing difficult, so horsemen commonly call the disease "strangles," because it looks like the illness is strangling the horse. If strangles was on a nearby farm, it would have no trouble crossing the fence lines to Angie's horses.

Contagious diseases spread rapidly when horses are housed in tight quarters, and this county was packed with horses on small, hobby farms. Angie's farm was only a few acres, and she had seven horses. Her fence lines bordered farms that had horses in equally crowded conditions.

In addition, most of the riders in the county utilized the local fairground to ride because their farms were too small to have riding arenas and there was little open land for riding trails. The fairground was notorious for spreading diseases, not because it was poorly managed, but because so many horses came there for clinics, shows, and evening riding in the indoor arena.

Angie went on, "Ann's vet, Dr. Hutchins, told her how contagious the disease is. Because Ann doesn't think her neighbor's horses have the disease, she asked Dr. Hutchins if he could have brought the germs to her barn on his boots. He said that was possible, but he didn't think so."

Knowing how common the disease is in this county, I had already vaccinated Mik, but I wanted to find out what Angie knew about this disease before I put her mind at ease. It was also the perfect opportunity to show Angie the value of having me in charge of her farm's preventive medical program - to handle these kinds of problems for her.

And I thought I'd keep Angie on the ropes for a while, because she had a marvelous sense of humor.

"Yes, it's possible vets or shoers, anybody who goes from one farm to the next, can spread diseases, but Dr. Hutchins is a fine veterinarian, and I'm certain he takes proper precautions to disinfect his boots when working on farms where infection is present.

"It's more likely Ann's colt got the disease directly from another horse. Ann rides with the Range Riders Club, and they have regular events at the fairground. She probably brought it to her farm from one of those events. But, the disease is so common around here, she could have picked it up any number of places."

When I was a child my orphaned filly contracted distemper. She looked miserable with a high fever and so much nasal discharge that she could hardly breathe. She quit eating and drinking and lost weight. I believe it stunted her growth as she never grew to be as tall as either her sire or dam. Yet, the old horsemen, those who considered themselves to be experts, told me not to worry, that it was "good for a young horse to get the disease and get over it." They would then be immune for life. Well, the experts were wrong. My filly got it twice, and since I started practicing I had seen horses die of the disease despite the best of care by both vet and owner.

Getting strangles is definitely not good for any horse. I wanted to make sure Angie knew more about this disease than any experts who might be advising her.

"First - getting the disease does not protect the horse from getting it again, and second - the horse can get sick enough to die, despite aggressive treatment. The best way to deal with this disease is prevention. By isolating sick horses in strict quarantine, and vaccinating those horses at risk, I can reduce the number of cases. In this county every horse is at risk."

Now Angie was really worried.

"Well, Dr. Hutchins told Ann there's a vaccine, but it makes some of the horses sick, and doesn't work every time. He said the vaccine can actually give some healthy horses the disease, and some get abscesses where they get the needle. So if there's no guarantee that the vaccine will protect Mik, I don't know what to do. I'm afraid Mik might get complications if we give him the vaccine, and he might get sick and die if we don't! What should we do? You know how long I waited for a foal from Special. I'd just die if anything happened to Mik!"

I had let Angie rant on, because I can serve my clients better when I understand clearly their concerns. So I got Mik's medications from the truck as Angie talked. While Angie worried about strangles, I was worried about the parasites foals can carry if not dewormed at any early age. I didn't want the ascarids that young foals have to grow large enough to block Mik's intestine when I killed them with dewormer, so Mik was already getting his second dose of dewormer, despite his young age. When Angie stopped for air, I took advantage of her concern to put her mind at ease.

"Angie, there is a newer vaccine available - newer than the one Dr. Hutchins described. It was tested at the vet college in their herd of broodmares. And while he's right, there's no guarantee it will protect an individual horse, evidence shows the illness is rare and milder in vaccinated horses, compared to unvaccinated ones. And the new vaccine does not contain any live bacteria, just one protein, so the vaccine can't cause the disease. I've used it on hundreds of horses in my practice, and on Rocky, so you know I believe in the value of the vaccine and I trust my own horses with it. I've never had a horse get an abscess at the injection site, but it can happen."

In my brief years in practice drugs were pulled off the market within the first year of release due to unforeseen complications. As a result of seeing the harm these drugs caused, I don't hurry to use the latest drug or vaccine. While these drugs have been tested enough to pass the drug approval process, sometimes complications are not evident until a large number of horses have received the product. I let other vets try the new drugs on their patients. I won't use my patients as guinea pigs.

By waiting a few months, no horses in my practice have had complications from these new 'miracle cures.' In a short time the bad drugs are gone, but the good ones will still be available and I'm ready to try them.

I never recommend any medication for my patients that I won't use on my own horses. I treat their horses with the same caution and compassion I have for my horses.

The new strangles vaccine was a big improvement over the previous vaccine. The older vaccine did cause illness and abscesses, so I was glad the new vaccine was available when I graduated. The newer vaccine did exactly what the researchers reported - reduced the number and severity of cases of strangles. While horses may get sore at the injection site, I get sore from my tetanus booster, too, but that's a small price to pay for protection. If the soreness is a problem, I prescribe a pain reliever.

As Angie slipped the halter over Mik's nose, I took his temperature. If he was incubating strangles, or any disease, it would be unwise to vaccinate him. He fidgeted and fussed. He was growing into a fine colt, and I was glad to feel his strength as he fought to regain his freedom from Angie's solid grasp.

"His temperature is normal. He can finish his boosters today."

I slipped the needles into his muscles, one in his neck, two in his rump, vaccinating him for all of the common diseases that occur near this farm.

"So, should we vaccinate Mik against strangles?"

"No."

"No! Why not? I thought you just said you *liked* the vaccine."
Angie was confused and consternated.

"I do. But I already gave it to him! You told me to take good care of him, and I did. That's why I get the big bucks, you know, not so much for giving the injections, as for making those decisions for you. If I'm handling his vaccinations, you don't have to worry about him.

"I know how common strangles is, and how deadly it can be, and I know how much Mik means to you, so I vaccinated him as soon as he was old enough. I made the decision for you, because that's my job."

Angie looked relieved.

"And you don't have to worry about a thing. He got all three doses without any problems. He's as protected as modern medicine can make him."

"You...you..." Angie was speechless.

That had never happened before.

"...you let me go on and on, through this whole story and you had already done it!"

"Yeah, I just wanted to show you what a great job I was doing for you and Mik!"

"You're driving me crazy! Let's go to the house for something to drink," Angie said as she walked out of the barn towards the house.

"And thanks for taking such good care of Mik. I'll tell Todd your bills are worth it."

"Yeah, but will he believe it?"

"He'd better!" Angie laughed and raised one eyebrow.

Chapter 14 Strong Irish Brothers and Well-bred Horses

It was a cold November morning, but the howling wind had not brought us any snow....yet.

Most of my emergency calls come in at feeding times, normally around sunrise and sunset. I try to make sure that feeding my horses is a simple procedure, as it may be cut short by an emergency. Today, the page came from Patricia Murphy just as I was putting Rocky's hay in his manger.

I rushed through chores and jogged to the house to return her call.

"This is Dr. Thibeault."

"Dr. Thibeault, my mare, Sunny, is down in the fence, trapped, and she can't get herself out. Please hurry."

"I'll hurry, but I doubt that she'll wait for me."

"She'll wait. I've called my brothers, and they're coming, but none of them are close by, and my husband left for work, so I can't reach him. Please hurry."

"I'll be right there!"

Clancy and I jumped in the truck and were off. Luckily, it was early, before rush hour, so traffic was light. If everything went smoothly, I might be done at Pat's before my normal workday started and not have to re-schedule my day's appointments.

As I drove, I thought about Sunny - trapped, injured and scared, lying uncomfortably on the frozen ground.

Horses rarely wait for someone to rescue them. I could count on the fingers of one hand the horses that were trapped when the client called me and were still down when I arrived. Most horses that get tangled in a fence fight against the pain until they are exhausted or seriously injured, inflicting further injuries from the struggle. Wild horses survived attacks from predators by running away, and anything that prevents them from running may cause them to panic.

Barbed wire, which was developed to contain cattle, is a major problem for horses in my practice. Nearly half of my emergency calls are a result of horses injured in fencing. And serious injuries to vital structures - tendons and joints - may be life-threatening.

Luckily Sunny had been imprint trained, a process made popular by veterinarian Dr. Robert M. Miller. Imprint training takes advantage of a foal's ability to learn rapidly right after birth. By exposing a newborn foal to potentially threatening stimuli, and showing the foal that there is no real danger, the foal relaxes and a strong bond forms between horse and human. These imprint trained foals have less fear. If the foal is also taught to yield to pressure, rather than fight against it, when it later becomes trapped, the foal soon finds struggling increases its pain, so it is more likely to stop struggling. They are also more willing to let humans help them. I hoped Pat's early handling of Sunny was paying off now.

When I drove down the lane to Pat's farm, I could see Sunny was still down in the fence, and, for the moment at least, resting still with Pat by her side. I couldn't tell if she was patiently waiting for help or if she was injured too seriously to move.

I grabbed my stethoscope and raced across the field towards Pat, trying not to startle Sunny. As I got closer, I could see the mare was in quite a predicament. She was in the corner where two fence lines converge, but this was not a normal corner. The fence lines came together in a sharp point, and the mare was trapped in this narrow triangle. She was down on her left side, and all four of her feet were sticking through the wire mesh fence. The corner was so tight, that her back was up against the opposite fence line. There was no room to pull her backwards out of the fence. To complicate matters, there was a corner brace, running diagonally from the top of the fence post at the mare's tail to the bottom of the fence post at the mare's head, and running between the mare's front and back legs.

The top of the brace was nailed to the top of the fence post, and the bottom was buried in the ground. At least there was no barbed wire.

How were we going to get her out?

Pat and I couldn't slide her, because there were fence posts on three sides and her legs stuck through the fence. If we had bolt cutters we could cut the wire mesh, but I didn't have bolt cutters, and I couldn't budge the posts anyway.

We needed help.

"Thanks for coming so fast, Dr. Thibeault. I called my brothers, Tom and Andy, as soon as I hung up with you and they're on the way with all the equipment they need. They're working at a construction site and should be rolling in the driveway any minute."

"Great. We're gonna need them. How did she get herself in such a predicament?"

"I dunno, 'cause I didn't see her go down, but we've had trouble with stray dogs running in our fields, and I bet they chased her into this corner. She probably tried to jump out to get away from the dogs, and got trapped in the fence. Her struggling wedged her deeper into the corner. See those marks on her rump? I think they're dog bites."

Pat stroked the mare's neck reassuringly. Sunny was alert but still. She was gentle and even-tempered by nature, and seemed to accept that we were there to help her.

Sunny's hindquarters showed fresh wounds that could be dog bites. She had a large wound to her chest, between her front legs, but her ribcage seemed intact, and her breathing was normal. I saw no external bleeding, but she could be bleeding into her chest.

I would deal with the skin wound once we got her on her feet, after I knew everything else was okay. I checked her vital signs. I couldn't assess the condition of her left side, but her right side and legs seemed okay. She did not have any other visible major injuries, but she was going into shock.

The fence post gave a clue to how Sunny injured herself. There were horse hairs ground into the top of the corner post, so Pat's guess about how the mare got trapped was right. Fortunately the old post was wooden and broad. The top was worn smooth from years of weather. The force of her chest on the post would cause major bruising, but at least there was nothing sharp to puncture her chest. I had lost other patients who impaled themselves on steel fence posts, causing damage to internal organs and fatal hemorrhaging. Pat's choice to use wooden posts instead of steel had saved Sunny's life.

I told Pat Sunny would be okay. I squatted down by the mare's head, stroking her and making small talk with Pat.

"Because she's so patient, she'll probably wait until your brothers come. We need some wire cutters, maybe a saw, and some more muscle."

"My brothers are bringing all of that."

I hoped Pat was right. The mare's temperature was below normal. She'd been on the cold ground for hours. The overnight temperature had been well below freezing. At least the ground was dry, so it would take the heat out of her more slowly than if it was wet. But hypothermia would set in if she didn't get up soon.

"Dr. Thibeault. Can't you just sew up her chest before she gets up? Won't that be easier?"

"No, Pat. With the fence in the way and her legs extended I can't reach the wound. She may have wood splinters in the wound, and I can't examine and clean it well while she's on her side. She may have injured the legs she is lying on, and could have serious internal injuries that aren't apparent. Once we get her up I'll re-evaluate her. Then we'll stabilize her, get her warm, and then tend to the wounds. She's not bleeding seriously from the wounds, so they can wait. I have to assess her whole condition before suturing the wound. It may be the least of our worries."

It was a relief to see the green Ford pick-up pull into the farm driveway. Pat's brothers grabbed tools from the back of the truck and sprinted across the field, tools in hand. Pat quickly introduced me to Tom and Andy.

The strong young men worked as a team and quickly removed the mesh fence around the mare's legs and behind her back. They dismantled the corner brace. The mare waited patiently while they made room to slide her out. We'd have to pull her away from the fencing before she could get her feet under her and stand.

As they worked, Pat calmed the mare so she wouldn't get up in the midst of the commotion. Before they pulled her free I cautioned them, "When she rolls onto her chest, don't encourage her to get up right away. If she stays on her chest for a few minutes, the circulation will return to the legs that were underneath her body weight. It will also help her balance if she gets up slowly."

Because horses weigh 1000 pounds or more, the circulation to the legs on the down side may be impaired if the horse is down on a hard surface for long. If Sunny jumped to her feet too quickly her legs might not hold her, and she could fall. We were in danger as well, and I didn't want anyone injured while rescuing Sunny.

"Pat, get by her head and whisper to her. Tom and Andy, you slide her rump out by pulling on her tail. Stay calm so she will."

With remarkable ease the brothers slid Sunny away from the remnants of the fence.

She rolled up onto her chest, and, with Pat's encouragement, rested there for a few seconds before she got to her feet. When she stood she was shaking, but kept her feet. A feeling of relief spread over both of us.

Sunny was not a palomino. She was a bay, Morgan mare, and had been named for her sunny disposition. She lived up to her name today.

We thanked Andy and Tom for their able assistance. They packed up their tools and went back work. They were truly life-savers. Pat and I would have never been able to free the mare without their help.

I examined Sunny, and the only serous injury was the chest wound. Although all of her feet had been through the fence, there was not a scratch on any of them. She had not struggled. Good for her.

Because Sunny's pulse was elevated, and her body temperature was low, she needed IV fluids.

"Pat, do you have a blanket? She's pretty cold."

"Yes, in the tackroom." Pat had no stalls, but had a room to store hay and tack.

Pat found the blanket and draped it across Sunny's back. We didn't close it over her chest, but Sunny wasn't going anywhere, so the blanket stayed put.

I got the fluids from my truck. I had run the heater on high all the way to Pat's farm, so the fluids were fairly warm, but I had to keep them warm as they went into the mare. I couldn't expose the IV bottle or the line to the cold air. The last thing this mare needed was icy fluids going into her veins. I also needed to keep the IV bottle above her heart, but there was no place to hang it.

"Pat, can you find me something to stand on?

"Sure, let me check the tack room." Sunny allowed me to I slide the IV catheter into her vein and tape it into place. I could see she was weak as her muscles twitched.

Pat returned with a chair.

"Will this do?"

"Yes. It's perfect."

I stood on the chair with the IV bottle inside my winter jacket - the fluids warmed by my body heat. I curled the line in my hand to warm the fluids as they went into the mare's vein.

Pat arranged for a trailer to take Sunny to a friend's barn for stall rest until her wounds healed.

After the fluid therapy, we trailered the mare to a heated barn, and I began cleaning the wound. The muscles had peeled away from the chest wall, but the chest wall was intact. Her lungs were okay.

"Sunny should do fine. She has only soft tissue injuries."

I had to practically stand on my head to clean and suture the wound on the bottom of Sunny's chest while Pat held a flashlight. Why don't horses ever get hurt in a place that's easy to see?

I never wanted to be a physician, but occasionally I am jealous of the advantages physicians have over vets. Human surgeons don't operate outside in inclement weather, unless they are assigned to a MASH unit, while I routinely suture wounds in freezing weather. Physicians have their patients roll over and the bright lights of the operating room let them actually see what they are doing.

I would have to go through contortions and fumble around in poor light today, but I loved working on horses and for horse people. I solved my problem by finding a small box to sit on under Sunny's nose while closing the wound. While it would be too dangerous with most horses, it was safe with Sunny - she was a cooperative patient.

Sunny's wound healed. She had several healthy foals and now proudly pulls a beautiful antique carriage. Her good bloodlines carried into the next generation. Her temperament and Pat's early handling were probably more important in her survival than the work her rescuers and I did that chilly November morning.

Chapter 15 Horses Don't Get That

Julie Bentley was a competent horsewoman. She called me to check her Saddlebred mare, Topaz, for pregnancy.

As I withdrew my hand from inside the mare, I was happy to announce "You'd better plan on having another mouth to feed soon. She is definitely in foal."

"Great, the sire is the reigning world champion, and I can't wait to see what he and Topaz will throw."

We discussed the mare's prenatal vaccinations and dietary changes to ensure a healthy foal as we walked down the shedrow. Julie was boarding two Arabian mares to help defray the costs of keeping her own horses. After the births of her two sons she quit her job, and the board provided some supplemental income. She enjoyed staying home with her sons, watching them grow up on the farm.

As we walked down the shedrow on the way back to my truck, I noticed that one of the Arabian mares had sores around her eyes and muzzle.

"What horse is this?" I asked. "I don't think I've seen her before."

"That's Susan Clark's filly, Silver Queen. Queen had a rough life before she came here. When she was just a yearling she broke her hind leg. Dr. Wight operated and saved her life, but she'll never be sound enough to be ridden. She's well bred and will be a broodmare when she's a little older. The leg doesn't bother her if she's not ridden."

I was not as concerned about the leg as I was about her skin lesions. The mare had bright red, scaly sores around her muzzle and both of her eyes.

"How long has she looked like that?" I asked Julie.

"Well, I never noticed it before. It's probably just sunburn. You know, with the high altitude and her pink skin, she's more sensitive than the other horses."

This was no sunburn. It was November. The sun was weak.

This mare was seriously ill with a rare condition. I had seen it only twice before, but I recognized it instantly.

Since the owner was not present, and I was not Queen's regular veterinarian, I couldn't legally treat or even examine her. I told Julie to contact Susan and have her call her regular vet right away.

"Are my horses in danger?" asked Julie.

"No. It's not contagious, but I am worried about the mare."

"I'll call Susan tonight when she gets home from class" Julie promised as I climbed into my truck.

The next day I got a call from Susan Clark, the filly's owner. "Julie tells me there's something wrong with Queen? What's going on?"

"I'd need to send a biopsy to the lab for confirmation, but she looks like she has an auto-immune disease."

"What? What's that?"

"It's called Pemphigus vulgaris. The immune system goes haywire and attacks the body's own cells by mistake. It's like she's allergic to herself. Queen's immune system is attacking specific areas of her skin, at the junctions between her skin and the membranes of the eye and muzzle. It is very rare, but I've seen a few other horses with the same disease. I'd need a biopsy to be certain, but she needs help. The disease can threaten her life."

"How can it be that serious, when except for those sores she seems okay? Julie says it's just sunburn. And I don't have any more money. Fixing her leg was expensive, and I'm still in college," moaned Susan.

"The best thing would be to take a biopsy to make certain. Call your regular veterinarian. Queen needs help. She's sick."

Vulgar means common, and this disease is called Pemphigus vulgaris because it is the common form of Pemphigus in dogs and humans, but it was not even mentioned in my classes in veterinary school as a disease of horses. In dogs, it manifests itself in sores around the eyes and muzzle. Queen's symptoms would be classic, if she was a dog.

The first case I had seen was several years ago, and the horse was being sent to California, so I don't know how the horse fared. The second case was an Appaloosa gelding. Because the owner was having financial difficulties, I paid the laboratory fees myself to verify my diagnosis. I was curious about this rare condition.

I first sent that gelding's skin samples to the local veterinary lab. Their technicians said they thought I was on the right track, but a lab in California specialized in auto-immune diseases, so I should send them a sample.

The California lab wanted the samples to be transported in a special medium, so I went to a human hospital to get the medium. I biopsied the horse again and sent the sample. A few days later the results came back. The diagnosis box read "Pemphigus vulgaris" but it was scratched out and replaced with "Pemphigoid-like syndrome, similar to Pemphigus vulgaris as seen in the dog. We've never seen anything quite like this. We'll look into it and get back to you."

Apparently the pathologist noticed that the sample came from a horse instead of a dog, and he knew horses weren't supposed to get this disease.

I never heard another thing from the lab. I was on my own.

I treated the Appaloosa gelding with steroids and he seemed to do well, but I never learned the cause of his disease. The horse lived near a nuclear facility, and I wondered if radiation was a factor. With diseases this rare, it is hard to find enough cases to determine the cause.

I called the vet college to speak to one of my former professors - a specialist in equine medicine, regarding Susan Clark's filly.

"This is Dr. Sheetz."

"HI Dr. Sheetz, , this is Dr. Thibeault. I hope you can help me with a tough case I've got. I have a horse with Pemphigus vulgaris. My text books have the drugs and dosages to use in canine cases, but I don't know how to adjust those doses for horses. Are you seeing any cases of it?"

"Oh, sure. I've seen a few of them - those greasy-skinned horses that shed their skin like a sticky dandruff. Special shampoos can be really helpful."

"No, that's Pemphigus foliaceus. I am talking about Pemphigus vulgaris, where the lesions occur around the eyes and the muzzle."

"Oh Marcia, horses don't get Pemphigus vulgaris!"

Great! The veterinarian I hoped could help me thought I was *nuts*!

How is it that when I was a student and Dr. Sheetz was the teacher, he knew all the answers? But now that I was in practice, with real cases not textbook scenarios, and I was asking the questions, he was no help at all. And on top of that, he doubted my diagnosis!

I had few options to help Queen, but I trusted my diagnosis. I'd seen it before, and I'd fight to get this mare the best help I could, even if it meant going against my professor.

In desperation I went back to Julie's farm to take photographs of Queen's sores so I could show them to some of my colleagues.

The first colleague I asked for help diagnosed Queen with sunburn. I reminded him it was November. He then said he was stumped.

Another colleague suggested it was cancer. Skin cancer was unlikely to occur spontaneously in several places at the same time. It was another dead end.

A third colleague suggested the lesions were caused by photosensitization. But horses suffering from photosensitization have lesions on all parts of their body that are white, and this mare had one white sock and it was perfectly normal.

Would Queen die before I could find someone who knew more about this disease than I did?

The annual meeting of the American Association of Equine Practitioners was coming up. I went to the meeting, photos in hand, asking all of the specialists I could find. Finally, one of my former professors said a friend of hers, Dr. White, was doing research on the disease, and had seen a few cases.

Bingo, I should get some help for Queen now!

I searched the seminar halls until I found Dr. White and introduced myself.

"Hello. I'm Dr. Thibeault, from Colorado, and I've seen several cases of Pemphigus vulgaris. I sure could use some advice on treatment."

I handed Dr. White the photographs of Queen.

"Well Dr. Thibeault, you know Pemphigus is very difficult to treat. Cures don't happen. Treatment is expensive, and must go on for life."

Finally, I had found someone who knew about the disease. And she didn't think I was a lunatic!

"Yes. I know. But I need to know the best way to treat these cases. There is so little information on this disease in horses, and when I have spoken to the other "experts" they think I'm crazy just because they are more experienced than I am."

As Dr. White examined the photographs, she reassured me "Well, you aren't crazy. This horse has Pemphigus."

I was relieved to find someone who had experience with equine Pemphigus. But, confirming my diagnosis was only the beginning. Treating the horse was the most important thing, in my eyes and in the eyes of the owner.

"This mare is young and I want to give her every chance. I found treatment protocols for dogs, and know that gold salts are used in people, but I need to know the best doses and combinations of medications for horses."

Dr. White outlined the treatment regimen that had been most successful for her. I thanked her and headed home, more confident that Sue and I could help Queen.

When I returned to my practice, I called Sue. She said she couldn't afford both the biopsy and the treatment, but she didn't want to lose her mare. Although it goes against my training not to biopsy cases before beginning treatment, I offered to treat the horse based on my preliminary diagnosis. The lab tests would only confirm what I already knew. The humane option was treatment. If the diagnosis was wrong, the treatment wouldn't work, so we'd know soon enough, and if I couldn't make my services affordable, Queen would die.

Susan refused the biopsy, but agreed to the treatment.

I met Sue at Julie's to begin the filly's therapy. She required an initial injection, and then medications daily for the rest of her life, which Julie or Sue could administer. I photographed Queen on the first day of treatment so I could document if she showed improvement. I would send regular reports to Dr. White, as any information I could provide would increase our knowledge of these rare cases.

I called Sue each week, and after two weeks she said the filly was much better.

When I checked on Queen's progress the results were startling. The skin lesions which were bright red and scaly had turned a healthy pink, looking much less irritated and painful. The mare was alert and eating well. She was trotting up and down the paddock.

Julie asked me "Do you think she'll regrow hair over those pink spots, or will she look like that forever?"

"I don't know. This disease is so rare that I can't give you any statistics. She's come so far already that anything is possible."

I took new photographs for Dr. White.

I refilled the prescriptions for Sue. I told her to call again when she needed more medication.

Several weeks went by, and I heard nothing from Sue. Then one day Sue called, obviously in tears. "Queen's doing terrible. She's worse than ever."

"What happened?"

"Nothing happened. Her sores healed, so I stopped the medication. I'm not rich, you know! But now she's even worse than she was *before*."

"Sue, you know she needs treatment for the rest of her life."

"Well, I'm busy with school, and don't go out to the barn very often. With her hurt leg, I can't ride her. And she looked so good I didn't think she needed the medicine. But now she looks awful. And besides, you never really figured out what was wrong with her. You never did the biopsy."

I was angry. I was fighting harder for this filly's life than her owner was. I had given the filly her best shot at a good life. The filly's response to treatment was dramatic, yet Sue still questioned my diagnosis - after *she* refused the biopsy!

"Sue, I know what was wrong with her, and so do you, because she responded so well to the treatment. It wasn't sunburn, or cancer, or anything else. The medications healed her sores. That proves the treatment was right. If you have any doubts, let's do the biopsy. We can schedule it for tomorrow."

"No. I just want you to put her down" she sobbed.

Put her down?

I was saddened that Queen's owner had given up when the treatments were working so well, but there was nothing else I could do. I considered calling Horse Helpers, but I knew in my heart that even they couldn't find someone willing to take on a young horse with such a severe and rare problem. And the medication might not work as well the second time around. Her previous leg injury meant she could never be ridden, and she was unproven as a broodmare.

I went to Julie's and examined the mare. The disease had indeed come back with a vengeance. The sores were much worse than before - larger and angrier. The mare was depressed, and off her feed. She looked miserable. At this point, the kindest thing to do for Queen was to end her suffering.

Julie and I went into her stall. I drew the euthanasia medication into the syringe, grateful that Sue had chosen not to come.

I had hoped Sue and I could work as a team to defeat this terrible disease, but every horse needs a dedicated owner on its side. Queen's owner had quit. Despite the incredible odds against this horse, humans let her down by ending a successful treatment.

I slipped the needle into Silver's vein, and in a few minutes she was gone.

I took more tissue samples and sent them, along with a new set of photographs, to Dr. White.

Maybe in the future, through Dr. White's research and sharing her knowledge with veterinarians treating these rare cases in the field, the need to destroy horses with Pemphigus would end - at least for horses whose owners didn't give up.

Chapter 16 Popcorn - The Sensitive Horse

I sprinted up the stairs to the kitchen just as the tall case clock in the hall chimed the last of its eight chimes. The phone was ringing off the hook. I had to grab it before the answering service did. I knew who was calling.

"Hello, Mary," I gasped into the phone, trying not to sound as winded as I was.

"How did you know it was me?"

"It's always you when the phone rings at 8 o'clock!"

I knew it would be Mary Wilkinson. The office opened at 8 AM, and Mary would call at the stroke of 8 when she needed an appointment. Her promptness forced me to finish my morning chores on time.

"You're gonna *yell* at me Dr. Marcia. Popcorn is too fat, but she needs her regular appointment. I want you to come out and paste her in the mouth!"

Mary created her own terminology, but over the years I had sorted it out. Mary understood the importance of regular deworming for internal parasites. While most of my clients choose to administer paste wormers themselves, Mary preferred that I come check her elderly mare and give her an oral dose of paste dewormer every two months. According to Mary, I either "pasted her horses in the mouth" or "liquidated them" depending on whether I chose a paste or liquid form of medication.

"Now Mary, have I *ever* yelled at you?"

"Well no, but you *might* when you see Popcorn. I swear, Dr. Marcia, I hardly feed her anything, but she's still fat. I admit that I've been too busy to ride her like I should."

Her spotted Appaloosa mare, Popcorn, seemed to manufacture calories out of thin air, and it was difficult for Mary to keep the mare's weight under control. Mary and I worked closely, discussing rations, weighing all meals, scheduling regular exercise, and regular check ups to monitor the mare's weight. She used the weight tape I gave her, which converts a measurement around the horse's girth to an estimate of the animal's weight. While it may not be accurate down to the last pound, it does show when a horse is losing or gaining weight, and can be a useful tool in the hands of a caring owner.

"Okay, I'll come see her next Friday. That'll give you seven days to put her on a diet and ride her so I won't *have* to yell at you."

"Well, alright. I'll do my best."

The following Friday, as I drove to Mary's appointment, I counted my blessings that I had clients like Mary. She was compassionate, knowledgeable, and committed to giving all of her animals - cats, dogs, and horses - the best possible care. She was always on time, had mannerly animals, and had them haltered and well-groomed before my arrival. The only time she ever complained was when she claimed I charged her too little for my services! When does *that* happen?

In my short time in practice, half of my emergencies were barbed wire injuries, which could be prevented by using safer fencing designed for horses. The rest of my emergency calls were due to colic, and most cases of colic were preventable with good management. Mary understood these principles and was committed to providing the best care for her animals, so I rarely had an emergency call at her farm.

I now had some wonderful clients, like Mary, who shared my passion for horses. On the days I visited those clients I really didn't feel like I was going to work. I felt like I was going to a friend's house to see her horses, and then we'd have refreshments and swap horse stories.

This was such a contrast from the first veterinary practice where I was run ragged treating emergencies, and I was forbidden to socialize with the clients. Considering the hours I worked, when did I have time to meet anyone besides clients?

As I pulled into Mary's farmyard, it was spotless as usual. Her new barn was painted green to match the house, and the horses even had a windsock in the corner of their paddock for decoration, although I don't think Popcorn was all that fond of it, as the wind could blow fiercely on the hilltop. The barn was well-equipped, with lights, a phone, indoor stalls, and a scale for weighing all rations.

I never saw manure in the paddocks. Popcorn and Buckwheat were tied near the parking area, and the well-used grooming kit was sitting on the ground nearby. The horses were clean, their coats glistening in the morning sun.

Mary was always ready, standing with the horses, and she was equally well-groomed. Her salt and pepper hair was perfect, and somehow she kept her clothes clean. I don't know how she did it. When I groom my horses, I always wind up with the horse's hair and dandruff all over me.

"Good morning, Mary."

"Where's Dr. Mom?" she asked, seeing that I was alone.

"Sunning herself on the beach in Delaware."

"Oh, good. I was worried 'bout her."

I got out of the truck, and let Clancy out behind me. This was one of the few places where I let Clancy out. Mary insisted that I give Clancy an "airing" and since it was a safe place I obliged.

Popcorn, the small, 23-year-old mare, was in good health. Her coat was glossy, her eyes were bright, and she was as anxious as ever to chase Clancy. Mary was such a conscientious owner that I'm sure she would know if one of Popcorn's hairs was out of place, which it never was. The passing years had meant that Popcorn's muscles sagged a bit, but she never tired on the trail and could keep up with Rocky when we rode the Highline Canal together.

Mary's buckskin Quarter Horse gelding, Buckwheat, looked fine as well. The large-bodied horse had very small feet, and suffered from Navicular disease, an arthritic condition of the feet. Mary bought him from an abusive horse trader who tried to sell the lame gelding to the highest bidder. We worked with her shoer, and most days Wheatly, as she called him, was pasture sound. When Mary brought him home, she begged me to help him live one more comfortable year. When she'd had him eight years, she reminded me that she had only asked for *one* more year. She didn't know that lame horses rarely die young - horses live forever if they're too lame to ride!

I dewormed the horses, and we discussed changes in Popcorn's diet between now and the next appointment. I complimented Mary on her excellent husbandry, and off I went to my next appointment.

"Come on Clancy. It's time to go."

Clancy continued to stare down Popcorn, ignoring my request.

"Clancy, come! I shouted. "The bus is leaving."

Clancy knew when I was serious, and although she was fascinated by Popcorn, she didn't want to be left, so she jumped in the truck. I bid Mary farewell and drove down the hill toward Denver.

I was surprised three hours later when my pager went off and it was Mary.

"Popcorn isn't right."

"What's wrong?" I asked.

"I don't know. But I went to clean out the corral at noon, and there was one less pile of manure than usual. She didn't clean up her breakfast, and she's moping around. She *always* eats her breakfast!"

"Is she rolling or sweating?"

"No. But she's not right."

"I'll be right there."

It didn't sound like a serious colic, and Popcorn was not pregnant, so whatever it was, it wasn't a life-threatening condition. But Mary knew her horse, and something was surely wrong.

When I got back to Mary's house, Popcorn didn't look much different to me than she had at the morning's appointment. Mary, however, insisted that there was something wrong with Popcorn.

I grabbed my instruments from the truck, but left Clancy inside, much to her dismay.

"I'm sorry, Clancy. Popcorn is too sick to play right now."

Clancy sat on the front seat, casting a watchful eye on the three of us.

I never argue with owners who report a problem, as they know their animals' habits far better than I do. If they say something's wrong, it's my job to figure out the problem. But subtle, vague signs don't give me much to work with, creating a diagnostic challenge. If I make the diagnosis early in the course of the disease and begin treatment right away, the horse usually does better. So I was under pressure now to help Popcorn.

Whenever faced with a diagnostic challenge, I remember Pischka and how hard I searched for an answer to her pain. I remembered how my pleas for help fell on deaf ears. The smug vets who didn't understand the problem dismissed my remarks. They made no effort to diagnose her condition. I was so grateful when I found the caring student at the vet college who diagnosed her liver problem. Years had passed, but I still remember how it felt when the vets didn't take my complaint seriously. I learned to trust a client's views about their animal, even when everything looks normal to me.

If I can't figure out what's wrong, I prove that I trust the client's judgment by offering to run tests to help find the cause. I never dismiss a client's complaint or show disrespect for their concern. I put myself in Mary's shoes for a moment. Something was wrong with Popcorn, and I would figure it out. I would not let Mary down.

I took the mare's pulse. It was forty-four. Mid-thirties is normal. That was high, but not alarming.

"Her pulse is slightly elevated. She probably has some pain somewhere, or an infection. The dewormer I used this morning is one of the safest available, and she has never had a problem with it before, so I don't think that's the cause."

I listened to her lungs, checked her nose for drainage, and took her temperature.

"Her temp is 100 even. No signs of infection. Lungs sound clear. Did she go down after you called me?"

Mary replied, "No. I brushed her before your appointment this morning and she hasn't been down since."

Popcorn had some minor lameness problems, but had only been ill once, with a respiratory infection. That wasn't the problem now. She was not in distress so I asked Mary for more information.

"Have you made any changes in her diet?"

"No. The hay is out of the same stack I've been feeding since August. I've been feeding out of the same sack of grain for a few weeks, since she only gets a handful of grain to entice her to eat her vitamins." I examined the hay and grain and could find no problems. In fact, the hay was so good that I had bought hay from the same farmer after getting his name from Mary last year. The grain was stored in rodent-proof containers and was fresh.

The problem was certainly subtle, and there was little to indicate its cause.

"Well Mary, I suspect an impaction colic. That can cause low grade pain, decreased appetite, and less manure production. I'd like to do a rectal exam."

Mary agreed, but the exam failed to reveal the cause. No impaction was within my reach, but the horse's abdomen is so large that it's impossible to reach it all. Her intestines weren't distended, but she had only been sick a short while. Impaction was the most likely cause of Popcorn's loss of appetite.

I told Mary my findings. I had to go with my intuition. But why would Popcorn be impacted?

Impactions occur in older horses that have dental problems and cannot chew their food properly, but Popcorn's teeth were excellent. I examined them twice a year, and floated off the sharp points annually. Impactions also occur if the horse doesn't drink enough water, and the feed gets too dried out to move through the intestine.

"Have there been any changes in her water?"

"No."

"It's been too warm for the tank to freeze, and I'm sure you keep her water clean."

"Yes, I scrub the tank every few days so the water is always fresh. And I use a tank heater when it's cold."

Indeed, the mare's tank was full of clean water.

"Does the water taste okay to you?"

"I haven't noticed any problems."

"Is Buckwheat okay?"

"He seems happy as can be."

"Well, I'm not positive it's an impaction, but that's my first rule out. I'd like to run some blood tests. If I get home in time, I can have the results for you by 8 AM. In the meantime, I'll treat her for an impaction colic. I have more appointments in this area, so if you notice anything else, or she gets worse, call me right away and I'll come back."

Sometimes clients will feel embarrassed that they are calling for nothing, and won't follow up. Even though I couldn't make a diagnosis on the spot, I wanted to be sure Mary didn't think I considered her a pest. I wanted her to know that I believed there was something wrong with Popcorn, even though I hadn't yet found the answer. Running the tests and medicating Popcorn showed my trust in her.

It was drilled into us in vet school not to treat any patient until making a diagnosis, but sometimes I had to help the horse before the test results came back. With practice, I was developing better clinical judgment, based on my experiences. I hoped my judgment would be on track today.

Mary agreed to the tests and treatments. I knew she would keep a close eye on Popcorn. She always did.

I gave Popcorn pain relievers, and passed IV fluids through a tube into her stomach to lubricate and soften any dried feed that may be causing the problem. When I said good-bye to Mary she looked a little more relaxed, but I knew she wouldn't be happy until Popcorn was on the mend.

I finished the rest of the day's appointments and hurried home to get the blood sent to the lab. As I had not heard from Mary, I knew Popcorn must be doing okay.

I called Mary for an update.

"She feels better since you treated her. She's eating again, and looks brighter, but she still isn't passing manure."

"Well Mary, if she ate less than normal, her manure production will be decreased for a while. I'll call you tomorrow as soon as I get the lab report. In the meantime, continue to keep a close eye on her. Your observations will help us figure out what's bothering her."

I needed her keen powers of observation to help Popcorn.

I called the lab first thing the next morning, and all the blood tests were normal. Great! The panel of tests picked up most serious problems, and Popcorn apparently didn't have any serious problems. But what was bothering Popcorn?

When I called Mary, she reported that Popcorn was doing fine and had no new problems. Buckwheat was still okay.

I stopped by Mary's farm later that day and left Mary some oral medication for Popcorn in case her pain came back. Luckily, Popcorn didn't need more medication. Her pain never came back.

A few days later Mary called me. She reported that Popcorn was fine, but that the water from her well had turned brown. Apparently a new neighbor was digging a well, which had disturbed the water table, and Popcorn was so sensitive that she detected the change in the water before Mary or her husband noticed it in the house.

Mary now has a filter on the water line to the house, and another one on the water line to Popcorn's water trough.

Popcorn is still contentedly munching hay in Mary's barn.

And Buckwheat's *one more year* stretched into 15.

Chapter 17 Love at First Sight

He was tall.
He was dark.
He was handsome.
He was young.
He was athletic - moving with the grace of a dancer.
He had the most beautiful brown eyes.
He had a playful side, and a gentle nature.
His name was Patrick.
It was love at first sight.
He was, of course, a horse.

The three year old thoroughbred gelding came to Horse Helpers shelter because he was in terrible health. He had come from a loving family, but his health problems were extensive and they could not stand seeing him suffer. They were struggling under his mounting medical bills. He was so young they did not want to put him down. They didn't know what else to do.

Horse Helpers had an arrangement with a thoroughbred rescue group, so placing Patrick shouldn't be a problem. It was my job to diagnose and treat his health issues, getting him on the road to recovery.

As Sandy, one of the Horse Helpers' volunteers, led the brown gelding out of his stall into the breezeway, I could see that Patrick was really something special. There was a fire burning in his furnace. The colt had been too ill to be ridden recently, so he was not fit, but it was clear that his bloodlines were excellent. He was the product of careful breeding to produce an outstanding athlete. I could easily envision what a gorgeous horse he would become if only we could make him healthy.

Sherry Edmonds, the founder of Horse Helpers, was just coming to the barn from the office. Sherry was meek by nature and deeply religious. After raising a house full of children, she and her husband now devoted themselves to caring for unwanted horses.

"Good to see you, Dr. Thibeault. Isn't he something?"

"He sure is."

In its early days of operation, Horse Helpers focused on old ranch horses - horses that were too arthritic for the demands of ranch work but were well trained enough to be placed with teenagers. The kids were usually lightweight, often rode bareback in the summer, and provided great homes for the horses. When the kids went off to college, the horse was either ready for retirement, or passed down to a younger sibling. But Patrick was clearly no old ranch horse.

Sherry told me "His owners reported that he would get stomachaches very commonly - sometimes every day. He had been treated repeatedly by their veterinarian, and fortunately had never been sick enough to require surgery, but the colics kept happening. The medical bills were more than they could afford, and they really wanted to give him another chance. So he wound up with us."

Sherry showed me his medical records. They were very sketchy. Patrick's vet had not tried very hard to solve his problems. There was no deworming history. There were no manure examinations for resistant parasites. There were no blood tests to rule out liver ailments or other causes. Nothing had been done to determine the cause of Patrick's problems, yet the owners had been charged a small fortune for treatments when he was sick.

Besides his colic, he was lame - in both front legs. The medical records showed he had been diagnosed with pedal osteitis, an inflammation of the bones in both front hooves, but no x-rays were taken to verify this diagnosis.

"The owners said the vet told them all Patrick needed was some potassium, and he would be fine. So they supplemented his diet with potassium, but Patrick did not get better," said Sherry.

Lack of potassium was not the problem.

"Colic kills so many horses, so you know there's a chance he may die before we can fix him."

"I know" said Sherry, "but we've got to try."

"We will."

"Sandy, can you walk him up and down the aisle please?" I asked.

Patrick walked very gingerly, placing each foot carefully on the level concrete. He was very sore.

"He can't control his youthful exuberance, so sometimes he races around the paddock when he's turned out, but he's always sore afterward," said Sherry.

Today Patrick was content just to walk. He was cooperative when I asked him to lift his hoof. His shoes were worn thin, and his toes were very long, which increased the strain on his tendons.

"He hasn't seen a good farrier in a while, has he?" I asked.

"No, I think his owners just gave up on him."

"Well, at least they brought him here, instead of to an auction, where he would have been sold to slaughter because of his size and his lameness."

"I'm glad he's here."

"Me, too. He's too nice to give up."

I ran my hand down his left front leg, and Patrick flinched in pain when I pressed on the suspensory ligament, and also when I pressed on his flexor tendons. When I checked his right front leg, the suspensory ligament was also sore, and the tendons bothered him there as well. This was going to be difficult. To reduce the strain on the ligament, I could change the shoeing angle to shift more weight to the tendon, and vice versa. If the horse was sore in both areas, finding a way to adjust his shoeing to make him more comfortable would be challenging. Patrick needed a special horseshoer.

The pain in his feet would be easier to control. Wide web shoes and pads would protect his feet. Good shoeing should give him immediate relief. We'd have him walking better soon. Trotting would be another matter.

We'd have to treat him without drugs. Pain medication can cause an upset stomach and even ulcers, and Patrick didn't need anything to upset his stomach.

Sherry and I outlined a plan of action.

"Call Scott and have him take care of Patrick's feet. I'll leave you a shoeing prescription he can follow, and have him call me when he's done. I'd like to hear any suggestions he might have after he gets his hands on Patrick."

Scott trained as a horseshoer at Cornell University and we had good results when working together treating lame horses. He shared my passion for helping horses in trouble. His broad, sun tanned shoulders and rough, calloused hands were the result of years of hard work, but his hazel eyes reflected the gentle soul within. Scott was the perfect choice because Patrick would need compassionate handling. His sore feet would make him uncomfortable when the shoes were nailed in place. Patrick would be a challenge, even for Scott.

"For his diet - feed him nothing but grass hay, and biotin, a B vitamin to strengthen his hooves. No pain meds - they can upset his stomach."

Thoroughbreds' hooves tend to have weak walls and thin soles. Biotin increases the strength of the horn that forms the horse's hoof, and speeds up growth. Patrick needed good quality horn that would be strong enough to hold shoeing nails, and faster hoof growth would speed Patrick's recovery. It would take months for that new hoof, which grows from the top down, to reach the bottom, so we needed to start today.

"Because most cases of colic are caused by internal parasites, we have to be conscientious about clearing out any he may have. Even after they are removed, the damage they caused will take months to heal. I'll deworm him today with a safe drug, but we need to keep our fingers crossed that he's not so full of parasites he gets a bellyache when we kill them. The records didn't show when he was dewormed last.

"Then it'll be up to Patrick to heal himself if we can support him long enough for that to occur."

Other causes of colic, like a diet that is too rich, or spoiled feed, or feeding after strenuous exercise wouldn't happen at the shelter. The trained volunteers at Horse Helpers didn't make those mistakes.

"I'll draw blood today so we can rule out other causes of abdominal pain, including liver disease."

I left Patrick in good hands, and did not expect to see him again. Thoroughbred rescue should take him.

Scott called when he had finished with Patrick. "I shod Patrick today, but the shoes probably won't stay on. I put on pads and wide webbed egg bar shoes, and he's comfortable. But he really was difficult."

"What do you mean?"

"He jumped all over when I picked up his left front hoof and put it between my legs to shoe him. The only place he was comfortable was when I got completely under him, when his shoulder was straight."

Having seen how cooperative Patrick was when I examined him, I knew he had to be in pain to fight with Scott. If pulling Patrick's hoof to the side caused him pain, he probably had a problem with his left shoulder, too.

Horseshoeing was hard work under any circumstances, but it is made even harder if the shoer has to position himself under the horse's elbow, instead of pulling the horse's leg out to the side. I was so glad for Scott's patience. He knew that this kind horse couldn't help but pull away when he was in pain.

I couldn't stress Patrick with an extensive lameness exam - an hour of trotting, poking, and prodding. Expensive tests, like nuclear scintigraphy and MRIs, were not in Horse Helpers' budget. We'd just work our way through his problems, beginning with colic and sore feet, and treat new ailments as they were revealed.

Since Patrick was already being rested and treated for his other ailments, his shoulder would have to wait. If he'd been healthy, some medicine might ease his pain, but an ulcer might push him over the edge. With rest, his shoulder shouldn't get any worse and it might even heal on its own.

"Thanks for the report, Scotty. I appreciate your help on this one."

"Keep me posted. I probably won't have to trim him for a long time. His feet hadn't grown much in the time it took him to wear out his last set of shoes. His walls are weak so I don't know how long those shoes will stay on."

At the end of the week I received a call from Horse Helpers.

"Dr. Thibeault this is Sherry Edmunds. I'm calling about Patrick."

"Oh, did you find him a home?"

"No, thoroughbred rescue refused to take him. He had too many medical issues for any of their adoptive families to take him. And he's been colicking every day at feeding time. When we put hay in his stall, he lies down in his stall and rolls up on his back for a few minutes. Eventually he stands up and picks at his food. He doesn't have much appetite, but his hay is gone by morning.

"Is there anything else we can do for him? I feel so sorry for him. He's in such pain every time he eats."

It is common for foals with ulcers to lie on their backs, but at 16 hands tall Patrick was certainly no foal. Ulcers can plague adult horses, but usually affect horses that are subjected to strenuous exercise, like racing or athletic competition, and horses fed high grain diets. Patrick was resting and fed no grain.

"His blood tests came back negative, so his internal organs are functioning fine, and he has no infections. It is likely parasites caused internal damage, and I dewormed him at my first visit. There's really nothing else we can do now for him, but be patient while the damage heals. Just stick to the bland diet of grass hay, and pick out the very best bales for him - no dust or mold. Keep it in front of him 24 hours a day, so he doesn't get stressed about running out of hay, and then get excited at feeding time. Scrub his water bucket every day so it is clean enough that you would drink out of it yourself. Then we just have to sit back and wait and see if he can heal himself."

"Okay, but I wish there was more we could do."

"So do I. But there really is nothing more to do, but treat him kindly and hope he lives long enough to heal himself. Sherry, he's so fragile that I'm afraid to give him any medications if we can possibly avoid it."

"Well, I agree. I wouldn't want to risk his health, but he has me worried."

"Me, too."

"I'll say a little prayer for him," she whispered.

"That may be the best treatment of all," I agreed.

On my next visit to Horse Helpers, Patrick was still there. I took a stool sample, and had it checked for parasites, to see if the dewormer missed anything. It didn't.

The shelter called me again about a month later.

"Dr. Thibeault, no one will adopt Patrick. Thoroughbred Rescue has tried all of its members again, but no one will take him on."

"Well, I can't blame them. Sometimes we get lucky, and find a nurse or someone with medical training who is not afraid to take on a challenge. Unfortunately, there aren't enough of those kind souls to go around."

"Well, you know that's sort of what we were thinking, so we thought it would be perfect if *you* took Patrick."

Me?

Rocky, my gelding, was living alone, and he was now a senior citizen. My neighbor's mares kept Rocky company over the fence, so I had not entertained the thought of getting another horse, but maybe Rocky would like a companion and I could use another riding horse.

But Patrick was both sick and lame.

Caring for Patrick would be expensive. He would require special shoes for months to come. He'd need to be treated with kid gloves so nothing would upset him. And there was no guarantee he would ever be sound or healthy enough to ride, or even that he would live...

With his history of colic Patrick might not live long.

How could I treat Patrick without getting a broken heart?

But, it had been love at first sight, so I said yes.

When I brought my trailer to get Patrick, I had to pay an adoption fee, like everyone else, even though I had treated him for free for months, and no one else wanted him. I was a bit miffed, but decided not to make an issue of it. I brought Patrick home the first weekend of September.

After his time in the shelter his bouts of colic were less frequent, but he still had several bouts a week. He lived in a box stall at the previous farm, and Horse Helpers put him in a stall to monitor his diet.

But on my farm he'd live outside as naturally as possible - with grass hay, water, sunshine, exercise and companionship - all the requirements of a happy equine life. I picked a small paddock, with shade and a windbreak. A stall was available if he needed it. The sandy soil eased his sore feet. I surrounded his huge feeder with rubber mats so he wouldn't pick up loose hay off the sand, and fed him psyllium to remove any sand he might ingest. I filled the feeder to the brim with fresh hay, so he would never get hungry. He could eat whenever he wanted, just like grazing, but there were no weeds to upset his stomach. I kept his water tank full and sparkling clean. He was turned out for a few hours a day in the pasture with Rocky. They got along marvelously. Patrick followed Rocky around the field, like a kid tagging along behind his big brother.

I didn't ride Patrick, or even brush him for the first few months. I wanted to eliminate all of the stress from his life and let him just be a horse, eating and sleeping and nothing else. I dewormed him so his intestines would not suffer further damage from parasites.

Horses normally shed their coats in the spring and fall, so each coat only lasts about six months. Rocky had begun shedding in August, and was now nearly ready for winter. Patrick did not shed as winter approached so his old coat was dry and dull. I blanketed him, as his owners before me had done, because his thin coat would not keep off the winter's chill. It can get pretty cold in Mountain View.

His appetite improved, but he still looked sick. Any coat supplements could be hard on his system, and might cause him to colic. His intestines probably couldn't metabolize his feed properly enough to support the growth of a new coat.

I had to be patient.

I found hoof trimmings all over the barn after the first shoeing, as Patrick was still too uncomfortable to stand quietly and Scott had to trim him while he fidgeted. But each time Scott came out to shoe Patrick, he got a little better. Over time, his pain decreased and finally he could stand in one place. As his shoulders improved, Patrick objected less when Scott placed his hooves between his knees.

Patrick now walked comfortably in his shoes with pads.

By Christmas, we shod him without pads. His hooves had softened under the pads, so he was sore at first, but in a week or so he was walking comfortably again.

I prefer to keep my horses barefoot in the winter because the shoes ball up with snow and ice making it difficult to walk, but Patrick's feet were too sore without shoes.

Healthy hoof was visible at the top of his hoof. By spring, there should be good hoof all the way down, so Scott's nails would be able to hold the shoes firmly in place. I looked forward to the day when Patrick's feet wouldn't hurt him anymore.

Through the winter his colics became even less frequent, occurring about once a month. They were always mild. I would find him lying down and groaning, but he would go back to eating in 30 minutes or so.

He was now comfortable galloping around the pasture with his shoes, building his muscle and stamina and enjoying life.

By the time the grass greened up in the spring, Patrick was feeling much better. He hated to be alone, even for a second. When he saw Rocky go out into the field, he would buck in his paddock. He could kick so high that his entire body was above the top rail of the fence, but he never tried to escape. When I came with the halter he would calm down and let me catch him, standing patiently while I haltered him so he could go out with Rocky. But as soon as he was free in the pasture he would run and buck. He had that spark in his eye, like a stallion the first day of breeding season. He was feeling much better, but his coat was still dull and dry.

In late spring, after the ground was softened by the spring rains, Scott and I decided to let Patrick go barefoot - free of the restriction of shoes. Patrick went "back to nature." The pain was gone from his tendons. Months of rest, a good diet, parasite control and proper shoeing helped him heal.

It was safe to add a protein supplement to his feed to put on muscle and grow a healthy coat. Rocky had begun shedding his winter coat in January, but Patrick still was not shedding in April.

As the hot days of May arrived, Patrick's dull coat was now a year old, and looking the worse for wear. The long, coarse hairs were turned up and dry from the sun. Grooming him was an exercise in futility and he still wasn't shedding.

In desperation, I clipped him to keep him cool for the summer. I wasn't riding him, but he galloped when I turned him out and the exercise made him sweat. His poor, old coat didn't dry out, like healthy hair. Overheating could be a source of stress, and I wanted Patrick as stress-free as possible. I left a small area of long hair over his back. It would cushion his back and prevent saddle sores if I ever rode him.

Nothing had changed by July, so I clipped that area off. It still hadn't shed, and was holding so much dirt in the damaged hair that I couldn't keep him clean. But Patrick was surefooted and energetic, so I began to ride him just a little - ten minutes a day around the sandy arena on the farm. He was delightful - willing, mannerly, and athletic. I could see the potential this young gelding had.

He was winning my heart, although I tried not to let him. His odds of survival still weren't good. He had suffered so many bouts of colic. I didn't hold out much hope that he would ever really be healthy. But I was softening my guard. His last colic had been four months ago. Maybe we would win the battle after all...

When fall arrived I had to blanket him against the cold. His coat had grown a little, but was still thin and dry. Patrick went through the fall in bliss, romping in the fields with Rocky during the day, munching hay all night long. I continued to ride him just a little, and he always was mannerly. Seeing how high he could buck in the paddock, I was grateful that he never chose to buck when I was aboard.

In November, Horse Helpers was having a benefit horse show, where they showcased horses they had rescued. They asked me to bring Patrick. I agreed, but I knew he was still not out of the woods. Hopefully the trip wouldn't upset him.

I got to the grounds early to ride around the empty coliseum before the spectators arrived. Patrick was excited, but controllable. We warmed up, and then went outside to await our turn. When we finally entered the arena, Patrick saw the formerly empty stadium now had nearly 5000 people in the stands. I thought the people looked and sounded like a huge, swirling monster. I can't imagine what Patrick thought, but he was petrified. He reared straight up on his hind feet and nearly went over backward - he was so afraid.

I slid off, and led him around the arena. As long as I was in front of him, between him and the crowd, he was fine. He put his face in the small of my back. He must have felt like he would be safe if he could hide behind me. At least I didn't have to put him in my coat, like Clancy.

Patrick no longer resembled the sickly horse I adopted the previous fall.

As I drove him home I reflected on his past. Since he was only three years old when he came to the shelter, and had been sick for a year, he really had very little experience under saddle. Breaking begins around two years of age, so Patrick had hardly ever been ridden. Considering that, he hadn't done too badly.

Rocky began shedding in early January, but not Patrick. I was beginning to doubt if he would ever look normal. Each season that he did not shed, his old coat got more dull and worn. This coat, which should have been replaced 18 months ago, had endured the strong mountain sun, rain and snow storms, and numerous mud baths and rolling in the grass, and it showed every bit of that damage.

Early one cold, February morning, I went out to the barn to feed. As was my habit, I placed my hand on Patrick's rump as I walked around behind him, tossing his hay in the feeder. As I pulled my hand away, my glove was covered with hair - Patrick was finally shedding!

In a month his new coat was beautiful! It grew in short, and thick, and was as soft as mink. He even developed dapples, which are a sign of good health. When the sun reflected off his new coat, it reminded me of one of my favorite gemstones - the tiger's eye.

For the first time since I met Patrick, he was feeling great and looking good.

Patrick might make it after all!

Chapter 18 Who Do You Trust?

It was a cold New Year's Day. As I peered out my bedroom window, the sun was shining brightly, and the ground was covered in a pristine blanket of glistening snow. The mountains were absolutely gorgeous - the snow reflected the sunrise in a pale pink hue. Mountain View was indeed appropriately named.

My pager went off while I was fixing breakfast. I guessed I'd be enjoying the view through my windshield, instead of from the kitchen table.

The call was from Bob Burns. Bob was a firefighter and a paramedic. I first met him last fall, when his mare Tiger Lily got injured in the fence. Since then I had been to his farm several more times to suture lacerations on his other horses, Cimarron and Bob. I asked him why a person named Bob would name a horse Bob. He told me the horse was already named Bob when he bought him, and he never bothered to change it.

When Bob, the firefighter, purchased his farm the horse paddocks were fenced in chain link. Bob didn't realize how hazardous chain link is around horses, but he was beginning to figure it out. So I shared some of my experiences with him, in hopes he would replace the fence and spare his horses injury.

I told Bob about a stallion in my care who decided to argue with the horse in the next paddock. They were separated by a six foot tall chain link fence. The stallion reared and struck at the fence, catching the heel of his shoe in the heavy gauge mesh four feet above the ground where he hung until I found him. Wire cutters weren't strong enough to cut the mesh, and I didn't have bolt cutters. I couldn't pull the stallion's shoe while his foot was stuck in the fence, and he was flailing wildly with his other foreleg. There was not enough room to work with clench cutters - tools that a farrier would use to remove the shoe without damaging the hoof. The horse's weight pulled half of his hoof off before we could get his shoe pulled, resulting in a severe injury.

Another time I was on a client's farm when her mare kicked at a neighboring horse through a chain link fence. She caught the point of her hock in the mesh and was trapped, hanging with her hind end suspended off the ground. The mare was small and there were enough people to support her body weight while we cut the fence away with bolt cutters. She did not sustain serious injuries, but she would have been severely injured if no one had helped her.

I've watched colts play with each other over the top of chain link fences. As a result, the top pole gets bent, exposing the sharp ends of the mesh. These ends are perfectly positioned to slice a horse's jugular vein, which would rapidly cause fatal hemorrhage.

Because of those experiences, I always advised owners to choose safe fence materials, but Bob's farm was fenced in chain link before he bought it. He wanted to settle his family into the house, and planned to replace the fence next spring. He pulled his horses' shoes for the winter, and hoped that would be enough to keep his horses safe until then.

After another emergency trip to stitch one of his horses in November, Bob vowed he would tear out the fence the next day. Because the ground was too frozen to drive posts, he would erect temporary corral panels.

I didn't expect to hear from him so soon, thinking his troubles were over.

"This is Dr. Thibeault. What's going on, Bob? Didn't you get the fence out?"

"Yeah, I did, Doc - every last bit of it. But Bob managed to get hurt anyway. He tried to jump over the top of the stall door, and tore up his hind leg pretty bad. I know what it's like to give up your holiday, Doc, but I had to call you. This really can't wait. I cleaned it up, and wrapped it, but it's gonna need stitches."

I knew that if Bob said it was bad, it was bad. He wasn't prone to panic over something minor. He had seen plenty of serious injuries working as a paramedic.

"I'll be right there."

As I put on my heaviest coat and thick gloves I wondered why horses never get hurt on a nice, warm day.

It was a cold winter morning, but the air was crystal clear and the sky was a deep, azure blue. The drive to Bob's place was beautiful. There was little traffic, as the people who enjoyed last night's New Year's Eve parties probably weren't enjoying the early morning hours of New Year's Day so much.

I drove south out of Mountain View through the rolling hills, admiring the countryside and grateful for Clancy's company. Today would be a good day. Bob was pleasant and helpful, the kind of man you'd expect a fireman to be. He was knowledgeable around horses, and very strong. Bob's tall frame was bulging with muscles, as the fire department had strict fitness codes. Bob had two teenage sons, and he encouraged them to work out as well. They lifted weights together in a workout room in Bob's house. I could see that twinkle in Bob's eyes - that competitive streak. Bob was not yet going to let his sons outlift him. I would be grateful for his strength if Bob, the horse, decided to be fractious.

As I pulled up to the barn, Bob, the fireman, was waiting for me inside. Bob, the horse, was in a stall, and Bob had done a good job of first aid on Bob's wound. The bandage kept the injured skin close to the underlying tissue, and kept it warm and moist. This was important on a frigid day like today, when cold air caused the blood vessels in the skin to constrict, reducing the blood supply to the injury.

"You've done a great job, as always, Bob."

"Yeah, but I wish I wasn't getting so much practice on my own horses."

"That's for sure."

As I unwrapped the bandage, I knew Bob was in for a long recovery. A huge, gaping hole was all that was left of the front of Bob's hock. Like the human ankle, the hock is a bony region of the body, criss-crossed by tendons and ligaments, but without muscle or fat to protect it. The skin was shredded and pulled to the side. Two major tendons were cut completely through, and the ends of the tendons had retracted several inches. The good news, if there was any good news, was that the joint capsule was intact, so the joint would be okay. Because the injured tendons were on the front of the hock, they would not be under tension when Bob stood, so they should heal over time. They would heal faster if I could stitch them together, but my stitches probably wouldn't hold because the joint flexes as the horse walks. If I could not save enough skin to close the wound, this type of injury would take months to heal and might require skin grafting.

"This is a nasty wound, but the joint capsule is okay, and I think I can fix the rest of the damage, with some cooperation from Bob. If the joint had been damaged, I'd send Bob to a referral hospital for orthopedic surgery. In spite of how bad it looks, Bob is pretty lucky. I'll sew him back together and hope it holds."

Sometimes the stitches don't hold until healing is complete, but even a few days of holding the wound together can reduce the healing time. I had to prepare Bob for the likelihood the stitches could pull out, but the surgery would still be worth doing.

"I'll put everything back in place, but the stitches may not hold. Even if they pull out later they will still shorten the healing time. The longer the wound edges are together, the smaller the scar and the faster the healing. Keeping healthy skin over the wound also decreases the risk of infection."

Bob had done a great job of cleaning the wound, so I gave the colt a sedative and injected some local anesthetic. Being a yearling colt, Bob was not likely to tolerate the sting of the local without a fight. When attending to his wound, my face would be down by his hind leg, where I could easily get kicked in the head. But Bob held him still, and soon the skin was numb enough to begin.

It was cold, but there was no way I could wear my warm winter gloves and stitch Bob's wounds. The thin sterile surgical gloves barely kept my fingers dry.

I sutured, and sutured, and sutured. First I pulled the ends of the extensor tendon back together and locked them down tight. Then I pulled the ends of the peroneus tertius together and locked them in place. My back was aching from being bent over, but I didn't dare kneel next to this colt. The cold was numbing my feet and making me stiff, but I was only half way through the surgery. I next pulled the edges of the skin together, aligning the ragged edges as best I could to cover the hole in Bob's leg. My fingers went numb, but I kept on sewing. By the time I was done, my hands were too numb to hurt anymore, but the wound looked better than I had hoped. There was enough skin to cover the opening, so the deeper structures were protected. Bob was lucky.

Bob watched over my shoulder while I worked. I am always more nervous when working under the judging eye of a medical professional, but I knew I had done my best.

"That looks pretty good, Doc. I didn't think it was all gonna come together."

"Well, before I went to vet school, my hobbies were doing jigsaw puzzles and needlepoint, so I'm pretty good at guessing where the pieces go, and putting them back in place once I figure it out. Now, it's up to you to keep Bob as quiet as you can. Do you have any heavy wire or rope? We're going to need to rig up a wire in his stall."

"Yes, I've got a roll of cable. Will that do?"

"That'll be great. You need to string it across the top of the stall on a diagonal, running from the feeder to the water bucket."

I rubbed my freezing hands as I walked to the truck for bandage supplies. My toes were as numb as my fingers. I jumped up and down and shook my hands, hoping to warm up enough to continue. I'd need a strong grip to apply a compression bandage over the wound.

While Bob put up the wire, I bandaged the wound in a Robert Jones bandage - a thick and heavy wrap which prevents the horse from bending his leg normally. It is not as rigid as a cast, but it was too cold for plaster to set today.

I returned to the truck for Bob's medications. My fingers were beginning to thaw. As I reached into the truck's refrigerator to take out the bottle of penicillin, I was startled to find that the bottle felt warm. My refrigerator must have quit running. I checked the thermometer on the inside of the refrigerator lid. It read 40 degrees. My refrigerator was working just fine. The penicillin, which was stored at 40 degrees in the refrigerator, was the warmest thing in my truck!

I gave the colt a tetanus booster, antibiotics and pain medication. I filled prescriptions for Bob to administer during the coming week. By then Bob had finished with the cable.

"Now, this is a new one for me, Doc. Are we putting Bob in traction?"

"Well, sort of. Because horses usually put their noses on the ground before they lie down, we'll halter Bob and clip his lead to a ring on this wire. That'll keep his head a few feet off the ground. He'll be able to walk around and reach his feed and water, but shouldn't lie down. That will lessen the strain on his hock joint, and help the stitches hold. "

The colt was fully awake as we hooked his lead to the wire. I checked to see that his lead was connected to the halter via a swivel, so he would not strangle himself.

"He should tolerate this just fine. He'll be free to walk around the stall. Keep him on the wire until I recheck him. I'll be back in three days, but call me before then if you have any problems, like the bandage coming loose or if he gets very sore."

"Thanks, Doc. I really appreciate you coming out so fast. And again, I'm sorry you had to spend your holiday sewing up my horse."

"You're welcome, Bob. Holiday work is just part of the job, for both of us."

"Happy New Year, anyway."

"Happy New Year, Bob. I hope this is not an omen of things to come!"

"Me, too."

As I drove home, I was absolutely numb with cold. I turned the heater on inside my truck. I took off my shoes so the heater could blast directly on my toes, but I couldn't feel the air coming out of the vent. I could only tell the temperature by reading the engine gauge.

I am always so focused on my patient that I rarely think to put the horse in a warmer place, like Bob's heated garage.

Focus is a good thing, but one of these days I was likely to get frostbite. Maybe there was a lesson to be learned here.

When I returned to Bob Burns' farm, Colorado offered up a mild winter day. The sun had been out since my last visit and melted the snow. The temperatures in the middle of the day were reaching into the 50s. It was a brief tease of spring, which was still months away. But these mild episodes are brief, and a storm was brewing. I had a light schedule today and hoped to get home before the full force of the storm hit, so I scheduled Bob's appointment for noon.

Bob was waiting in the barn when I got there. I love it when clients respect my time.

"It's a nicer day today, huh Doc?"

"Yeah. Much to my liking. How's Bob doin'?"

"He's tolerating the stall pretty well. I took him off grain like you suggested, and I think it's helping him stay a little quieter."

As I took the bandage off, I was hoping the stitches were holding. I peeled off layer after layer of padding and gauze, and the bandages were nearly dry. If the stitches had pulled through, there would have been fluid draining from the wound. When I got to the final layer, the wound looked as good as when I finished suturing it. I was delighted!

Bob was watching over my shoulder. "It looks good doesn't it?"

"Yeah, Bob. I couldn't be more pleased."

The wound edges were slightly swollen, and all of the skin was intact around the sutures. I cleaned the wound and applied a fresh bandage.

"Bob, you've obviously done a great job of keeping him quiet. Whatever you're doin,' keep doin' it. I'll be back next Saturday to check on him again and change the bandage."

As we walked back to my truck, I could see the storm clouds on the southern horizon.

"Looks like I can make it home before the storm hits."

"Yeah, it'll be my night to work in the storm tonight. My shift begins at 2 PM," said Bob.

"Well, maybe it'll be a quiet night."

"We almost never have a quiet night when it snows. We always have traffic accidents, but at least fires will be less common now that people have taken down their Christmas trees."

"Well, good luck to you."

131

I drove home watching the storm clouds over my shoulder, but feeling optimistic that Bob was on the mend.

When I returned to Bob's four days later, he gave me a troubling report.

"He's getting rambunctious. When I muck out, he tries to kick at me. I have to tie him in Tiger's stall. He's figured out how to sit down."

"Sit down?"

I have only seen trick horses sit. In nature, horses stand and lie down, and only go through the sitting phase momentarily when getting to their feet.

"Have you seen him sitting?"

"Well no, but his tail is full of shavings all the way to the top in the morning. He doesn't have any shavings anywhere else on his body. How could he wind up with shavings at the top of his tail except by sitting?"

"I don't know. I guess you're right."

Go figure.

I bent down on one knee to remove the bandage. The wound was a little more swollen and oozing, but all of the stitches were still holding. As I gently cleaned the wound, the colt showed his displeasure and began fidgeting. Bob was trying to hold him, but the lack of exercise was getting the best of our patient. He flexed his hock and then kicked out behind. Right before my eyes, the skin tore. All of the stitches were intact, but the wound gaped open.

Bob had not seen what happened because he was struggling to control the fractious colt.

"You okay, Doc? Did he get ya?"

I took a deep breath.

"Nah, he missed me, but the wound just blew apart. All of the stitches tore through."

"All of 'em?"

"All of them. But he'll be okay. The healing will just take more time. There's no sign of infection. And the wound is much smaller than a week ago. If we hadn't sutured it, I'm sure he would need a skin graft to close it. But it should close without grafting."

Instead of first intention healing – healing assisted by suturing the wound edges in close contact, Bob's wound would now have to heal by second intention, which is the natural way. The body forms a layer of granulation tissue to support the new skin, which then grows across the wound. First intention is faster and leaves less of a scar. In the front of the hock, the constant movement as the horse walks delays wound healing, and sometimes proud flesh can develop, when the pink, bumpy granulation tissue grows faster than the skin can close over it, and bulges out of the wound.

I rebandaged the colt's leg, showing Bob how to apply a Robert Jones bandage. Bob had learned many types of bandages during his training, and he would become an expert at this one before Bob's wound was healed.

"Put him back on the wire for as long as he'll tolerate it. Call me if you have any problems."

"Thanks, Doc."

As I drove home, I was glad Bob had such a good caregiver. His owner had medical training, patience, compassion, and strength, all of which would be tested in the coming weeks.

We stayed in touch over the phone, and the wound was healing well, but the colt was getting more and more difficult to handle. The lack of exercise was becoming a serious problem.

One day in early spring, I received the call that I had been expecting.

"Doc, I can't keep him in the stall anymore. The confinement's driving him crazy. What can we do?"

"It's time to take him outside and hand-walk him. The fresh air and light exercise should help him."

"I tried that and he went nuts. He tries so hard to get away that I can barely hold him. He nearly flipped over backwards twice yesterday. I thought one of us was gonna get hurt, and it might be me this time!"

"We can't have that."

I had to help both of them. I would sedate the colt to take the edge off of his enthusiasm, and turn him out in a small paddock, hoping the sedative would keep the colt quiet enough not to re-injure his leg.

"Okay, Bob. I'll come out tomorrow and give him a sedative, and we'll turn him out. Do you have a small paddock?"

"Just the one behind the barn. It's pretty muddy, and has a small slope, but it's only about 60 feet long."

"Well then, it'll have to do."

"What time will you leave for work tomorrow, Bob?"

"I'm off until the weekend."

"Great. I'll come tomorrow. You'll need to keep an eye on him until the sedative wears off, so don't plan anything else for the afternoon. I'll see you at one."

"I'll be there."

Again, I welcomed the fact that driving to the farm allows me to solve my patients' problems before I arrived. I value this quiet time to think. This is why I was one of the last veterinarians on the planet to get a cell phone.

I had hoped to get a few more weeks of healing before letting the colt exercise. The tendons would not be strong yet. One bad step and they could pull apart. But I couldn't risk Bob being injured by the colt. We would use the small paddock. It was the best we could do.

The dose of sedative was critical. Too much sedative would make him unsteady on his feet, and a fall could be as bad as galloping around. Because I had sedated him to suture the wounds, I checked my records to see what dose I used before and how he responded. Then I selected the dose.

The spring thaw was underway. The clay was heavy and wet from melting snow, making the footing slick, while the ground underneath was still frozen solid. There was nothing I could do about the footing. If we tried to trailer Bob to an indoor arena, he probably would hurt himself loading in the trailer, as he was not an experienced hauler, and he was out of patience from his confinement.

Bob and Bob were waiting for me as I drove in.

"Hi, Doc."

"Hi, Bob."

I filled the syringe with the drug that I hoped would help the colt overcome his excitement at being turned out.

"I knew we'd have to sedate him sooner or later for his first turnout. I'd just hoped it would be later. If he was a few weeks further along the tendons would be stronger and I'd be less worried. But it's out of our hands now. It's up to Bob. Let's hope this works."

I injected the sedative intravenously so we wouldn't have long to wait. Bob soon lowered his head, and when his head was hovering around his knees, it was time to go.

"He's ready. Take him out back Bob. I'll keep a hand on his hip to steady him through the doorway."

Bob led his staggering horse out into the paddock.

"Take him to the middle before you let him go, so if he falls he won't hit the fence."

He took the colt to the center of the paddock.

We'd soon know if I had picked the right dose.

My heart was in my throat. This colt's life was on the line. If my surgical repair didn't hold - if the tendons blew apart - he might damage the leg beyond repair. After all of our efforts, and all the colt had endured, today might be the day we'd have to euthanize Bob's colt.

Bob unsnapped the lead. It took the colt a moment to get his wits about him, but he soon realized he was free. He tried to gallop, but was having trouble getting his feet under him, due to the slippery clay and his impaired condition. There was no way to help him, so Bob and I just got out of his way. After skating around in the mud, Bob finally figured out how to keep his balance, and took off running across the top of the slope. As he crested the slope and began running down the other side, he saw the fence coming at him fast. The colt planted his back feet to stop, but the mud wouldn't hold, so Bob slid down the hill with a sliding stop that would make any reining competitor proud. His form was perfect. Better yet, his tendons held! Maybe the mud was a good thing after all, allowing his feet to slide!

"His leg is okay!!"

Bob and I were ecstatic. The hard work paid off. The colt was going to be fine.

Bob continued bandaging the wound and giving Bob limited exercise. The wound healed without grafting, and the tendons worked perfectly. He has permanent scars, but they don't cause him any pain.

Bob broke Bob to saddle later that year. When I visited Bob for our regular fall appointment, I was interested in his colt's progress, and the look on Bob's face told me he had a story to tell.

"Well, Doc, I wanted you to know the first time I rode Bob I took him to Steve Johnson's place. The whole time you were treating him, Steve told me the injury was so serious the colt would never be strong enough to be ridden. He told me you were ripping me off, charging me for treating a horse that would be worthless. So the first chance I got, I rode Bob over there to show Steve he was wrong."

I had no idea that Bob was under pressure to stop treatment, but I was glad he didn't give in.

"Well Bob, thanks for believing in me. I thought we could save this one, and I'm glad your neighbor couldn't convince you otherwise."

"Yeah, Doc, and I'm sure Bob's glad, too!"

"I'll bet he is!"

As I drove home that evening I was really glad Bob had not told me about his neighbor earlier. If he had doubted me, I might have doubted myself.

I did smile thinking of Bob, all six feet of burly firefighter, riding his sound young colt to the neighbor's farm and the look on Steve's face.

That picture would be priceless.

Chapter 19 Annie's Point of View

My clients, Bert and Dennis Simpson, share a great sense of humor. Dennis has a deep, booming laugh that is highly contagious and Bert is so creative that Dennis laughs often. They own Missouri Foxtrotters - horses noted for their easy-going dispositions and comfortable gaits. Most of their friends own Quarter Horses or Arabians and have never seen a horse foxtrot. Bert and Dennis grew tired of people who would watch them ride and scold them with "Is your horse lame?"

One day I found myself in the company of such a person. I was caring for two horses, a Foxtrotter and an Appaloosa, for some clients who drove trucks across the country. I occasionally rode the horses to keep them fit, and would invite a friend to join me. They were both good horses, but the fox-trotting gait was much easier to ride. So I always rode the Foxtrotter, and let my guest ride the Appaloosa. On one ride, my guest was complimenting my riding style, saying she hoped someday she could sit so still and look elegant like me.

Instead of telling her that it was the horse making me look good, not my technique, I just thanked her for her remarks. She'd figure it out someday, but in the meantime I'd graciously accept her compliments.

Foxtrotter owners say you can ride one your whole life and never really learn how to ride a horse, because they are so comfortable. Their t-shirts say "To Ride One is To Own One," but

I've borrowed their horses and after you ride them they always want them back!

One September day I was at the Simpsons' ranch high in the mountains, treating their horses for routine ailments. When we finished, we headed up to the house for some refreshments. As we walked up the slope to the cabin a beautiful flock of Canada geese flew overhead, in their classic V formation. Dennis asked me "Do you know why one side of the V is longer than the other side?"

I try very hard to answer all of my client's questions, and I especially fancy myself to be an expert on animal behavior. Besides attending seminars, watching videos, and reading books by today's horse whisperers, I had trained under some experienced international trainers, and was a licensed instructor myself. But my expertise extended far beyond equine behavior.

I took courses in animal behavior at the University of Colorado from Dr. David Chiszar, a brilliant professor and captivating lecturer. We studied everything from "running" snails through mazes to herding behavior in horseshoe crabs. In another course we studied the behavior of wild animals in captivity, meeting at the Denver Zoo. Students were allowed to go behind the scenes and follow the keepers on their rounds. I got to feed orphaned animals and observe the animals after hours, when the zoo was closed to the public. I talked to the keepers, who have a wealth of knowledge about animal behavior, and accessed the zoo's library.

I followed that course with an independent study in Yellowstone Park, following a herd of wild elk, noting how their behaviors differed from those of the zoo's captive herd. I wrote a thesis for the zoo's director, describing how management changes could result in more natural behavior within the elk herd.

Yes, I was indeed well versed in animal behavior.

In addition to the coursework, the year before I entered veterinary school I read over 50 books on animal behavior, including books on antelope, coatimundis, coyotes, dolphins, elk, elephants, prairie dogs, tigers, whales, and wolves. Konrad Lorenz's book on animal behavior introduced me to the concept of "imprinting." Adolph Murie's research on wolves in Alaska and his brother, Olaf's text on elk behavior gave me insight into predator/prey relationships. Hediger's book on the behavior of wild animals in captivity dealt with circus animals. I had even read an entire book devoted to bird migration.

Surely I could answer Dennis's question if only I thought hard enough!

As we reached the deck stairs, my mind was racing. I remembered that birds can migrate across large expanses of open ocean, and that it was felt that the magnetic pull of the earth's poles somehow helped the birds navigate when no land was in sight. I remembered that some species of birds were able to migrate long distances instinctively without the presence of older birds that had flown the route before. But I didn't remember coming across any research describing why the Canada geese don't have symmetrical Vs when they fly.

Perhaps physics was the answer. Is there less drag if the V is asymmetrical?

Before I could answer Dennis' question, he said "because there are more birds on one side." Dennis laughed heartily!

Duh!

We went into the cabin and Bert fixed some iced tea as Dennis and I settled around the kitchen table. Dennis told me their gray Foxtrotter mare, Annie, was such a character, that Bert wrote a column in her riding club's newsletter describing the world from "Annie's Point of View." According to the Simpsons, the seemingly normal mare I had just examined had a not so pleasant temperament.

It seemed as if the Simpsons were injured so often that when anyone in the riding club was injured they were named an "honorary Simpson."

Bert brought the tea and joined us around the table telling the story of an accident Dennis had last year - from Annie's point of view.

Bert began:

"We had gone for a lovely trail ride in the state park. Mr. Boss was riding me, while Mrs. Boss rode that new blond *hussy* they just got. Oh how I hate her! And little Boss and Molly stayed home, so little Boss could do his schoolwork.

"We were riding down the trails with Angie Palmer riding Special and her husband Todd on that gorgeous palomino stallion,

Glint of Gold. You know, I just have a thing for tall, blond stallions. I mean, he's so muscular, and handsome, and, and, well, you know, well-endowed. I mean, I think blond stallions really go great with gorgeous gray mares like me.

"I tried to get close to GG, because, you know, he's a breeding stallion, and you know, I'm available.

"At the lunch break GG and I grazed together under the shady canopy of cottonwood trees. It was so romantic, with the rushing waters of the creek nearby. Just when I thought we were hitting it off great, Mr. Boss and Todd decided it was time to get going. But we had a lovely afternoon, GG and I, walking stride for stride down the trail. Mr. Boss and Todd were much too busy talking to each other to bother us.

"When we got back to the trailhead, for some *insane* reason, Mr. Boss asked Todd if he thought GG could keep up with me, and challenged him to a race. You know, I'm noted for my speed. I just never know when I might have to escape from a saber-toothed tiger or some other monster, so I try to keep myself in shape. It shows, doesn't it?

"Well, we ran off and I took the lead, just toying with GG as I ran in front of him. But you know Mr. Boss didn't pick a very safe place to run. The footing wasn't manicured, like the race track I deserve. It was all torn up from those ugly fat horses pulling manure wagons through the mud. Can you imagine?!

"As a result of Mr. Boss's crazy idea, I slipped and fell. *I could have gotten hurt* if it wasn't for Mr. Boss's quick thinking. He threw himself down in front of me, so when I rolled over I didn't get hurt because I landed on him instead of on that hard dirt.

"I really appreciate his thoughtfulness.

"But as I got up and shook myself off, Mr. Boss said some words that a delicate filly like me really shouldn't hear. I didn't know Mr. Boss could talk like that!

"And can you believe it? They just ignored me! There I was, all hot and sweaty from working all day, and then having that nasty fall and getting mud on my beautiful hair. I needed a shower and a massage for my sore muscles. And GG was standing *right there*, watching everything. I was so embarrassed. But no - I get ignored by both Mr. Boss and Mrs. Boss.

"In a few minutes, a large sort of horse trailer looking thing with flashing lights and a bright orange stripe on the side came and picked up Mr. Boss and took him away.

"Finally Todd came over and took my saddle off. That hot sweaty thing was hiding some of my best features. He loaded me in the trailer with GG and we had a romantic ride home together, to GG's place. I even got to spend the night in GG's barn, so it wasn't all that bad, although we did have separate stalls.

"In a few days I was home again, but Mr. Boss didn't come out of the house to see me for a month! I was so lonely, having to wait for his attention, and dealing with that blond *hussy* that kept trying to steal my hay!"

By the time Bert finished, Dennis and I were rolling with laughter.

Poor Dennis had severe internal injuries, and was laid up for quite a while. He finished the story for me, from his point of view.

In the hospital the nurses all asked what happened, and horse people come like flies to honey when there are horse stories to swap. Dennis had an office job, but shod horses at night. His hands grew strong and rough, typical of hard-working farriers. While he was in the hospital he was introduced to a cute little nurse, so young that Dennis thought she was a Candy Striper, but she claimed to be a farrier also. Dennis doubted it, until they shook hands, and this cute young girl almost crushed his hand with her strong grip. There was little doubt that she was indeed shoeing horses.

Dennis told me his savior in the hospital was a nurse who told him to hug a pillow when he coughed. Coughing can be extremely painful with a fractured pelvis, and Dennis said he would be eternally grateful for her suggestion, which helped immensely.

Dennis fully recovered, and is riding again, but I don't think Annie and the blond hussy ever did get along.

Chapter 20 The Charro

It was Saint Patrick's Day as Dr. Mom and I waited in the barn for the arrival of our next client. We had finished our morning appointments with a little time to spare, so I grabbed a quick lunch and brought it to the barn. We were waiting for Juan Vargas. I hadn't officially opened my clinic yet, as improvements were still incomplete, but appointments that could be done on the parking lot were being scheduled. Juan was hauling Diablo to the farm to save the cost of a farm call.

While Clancy would normally be tending to Rocky, since I was eating, she found me to be more interesting at the moment. Clancy makes herself available any time human food is being consumed, but she is so cautious. She acts as if she thinks someone is trying to poison her. While my previous dogs would ravenously consume any food offered, and sometimes a piece of the hand holding it, Clancy was very careful.

I offered her a single potato chip, which she gently took from my hand and carried across the barn to the far end. Then, as was her habit, she put it down and looked at me. Then she sniffed it, picked it up and turned it over and put it back down. She looked at me again. Then she licked it and looked at me again. Finally she picked it up, chewed it and swallowed it. She is the only dog I know gentle enough to carry a potato chip in her mouth and not damage it. But why she does it, I'll never know.

Juan worked as a mechanic, and when I attended to his horse after working hours, his clothes and hands were covered with grease.

143

The hard work showed on his calloused hands. But today was different. He and his black stallion Diablo were going to be in the St. Patrick's Day Parade with other members of the Mexican Rodeo Association.

I heard Rocky whinny from his paddock, and knew Juan must be here, although I didn't see Juan's trailer. It's handy to have a watchhorse, since my watchdog was too busy with her potato chip to notice Juan's arrival. For some reason he had parked on the road in front of the farm. I first saw him as Diablo dragged him down the drive.

Today was clearly a special day. Juan was dressed in his finest Mexican charro costume - gray slacks with silver conchos down the side, a dress shirt and trim-fitting tailored jacket, and a huge Mexican sombrero shading his head and shoulders. He was polished to perfection. Diablo was spotless and his black coat glistened in the sun.

"My, what a handsome pair you are!" I called to Juan.

"Gracias."

Juan was to meet the rest of his troupe in just an hour, and needed a health certificate to enter the parade grounds. Diablo certainly was the picture of health. Obviously Diablo had fully recovered from his colic - no more prune juice for him! He pranced sideways down the driveway, looking proud and regal. Somehow Juan managed to stop him by the time they reached the clinic entrance, and I went to work examining Diablo. His coat was shiny, his eyes were bright, and he had no nasal discharge. His temperature was normal. I got all of the necessary information from Juan and filled out his travel papers.

Diablo dragged Juan back up the driveway to his trailer. Diablo jumped into the trailer and they headed off to the parade.

However, a few days later Juan was back with another horse. He called me about his young colt that had a painful lump on his leg. He trailered the colt to my farm the following Saturday morning.

Juan parked his trailer in the driveway as I came out to greet him. His colt was stomping angrily inside the trailer, rocking it from side to side and even rocking the truck.

"Hola, Juan. Como esta?"

My high school Spanish only took me so far, but at least I made the gesture.

"Bien. But I'm really worried about my Cisco. He has a bump on his leg that's really painful."

"Which leg?"

"His right foreleg."

Cisco was making such a racket in the trailer that I thought he might be too much to handle when Juan unloaded him. I remembered one of my professors, Dr. Turner, telling me "You know you're in trouble when your client unloads his horse and it looks like he's flying a kite."

"Juan, let me look at him in the trailer. We'll only unload him if we have to."

There was a small escape door in front of the trailer, by the colt's chest. Juan opened it so I could examine Cisco's foreleg. I saw the lump Juan had noticed. It was on the inside of the cannon bone, the major bone below the horse's knee. The lump was hard, hot and when I touched the lump, Cisco pulled back in pain.

"What kind of work are you doing with this colt, Juan?"

Juan was excited to tell me how talented this new horse was. "I'm getting him ready for the Mexican Rodeo. We are teaching him to gallop and spin. Amiga, he is good! He's a fast learner, and doing very well. He's even better than Diablo!"

This lameness was easy to diagnose.

"Cisco's problem is a fresh splint. The covering of the bone was damaged, probably when he was spinning he hit his leg with the shoe on the other front hoof. It can strike the bone hard enough to disturb the bone covering called the periosteum. The periosteum reacts like the bone is broken, and deposits calcium where it's injured. That's why the bump is so hard. In time, splints cool off, and it won't bother him, and often they shrink in size over time.

"But, Juan, you are working this young horse too hard for his age. He's just a baby. His bones aren't strong yet, and he doesn't have the muscle tone and coordination to work tight spins at high speed. He needs to grow up and build his strength and balance with longer, slower rides and big circles before asking him to do such tight, strenuous work. I can treat this injury, and he'll recover, but he'll injure himself again if you don't give him time to mature."

"But he is doing so well, I hate to rest him."

"Right. He's doing so well that he's lame and at the vet's for treatment."

Juan didn't answer. I stayed silent and gave him a chance to think. He was working Cisco so hard - hard enough to injure him, just because the poor colt had talent.

"If Cisco is as good as you say, then he's worth the time to let him grow, so he can be a good performance horse for you for a long time. If you ruin his legs now, you'll be looking for another good horse next year."

"You're right. He is too good to risk," Juan reluctantly agreed.

I know how hard it is to be patient with these young horses, but bringing them along too fast can ruin them before they live up to their potential. Juan didn't like what I told him, but at least he could see that it made sense. Having helped him with Diablo, I hoped I was beginning to build Juan's trust.

I gave the colt some pain medication and bandaged his leg with a poultice to draw out the swelling. I told Juan to hose Cisco's leg with cold water three times a day starting tomorrow to take the heat out. I prescribed a rest from strenuous exercise, and told Juan to ride the horse on some long, slow conditioning rides to increase the horse's fitness and coordination before resuming hard training.

"You have to build up muscle, stamina, and coordination before you go on to more difficult work."

I also recommended that Juan put protective boots, called splint boots, on Cisco's lower legs to protect against a similar injury in the future, especially when he was teaching the horse something new, or when working him until he was tired.

I had only been taking care of Juan's horses for a few months, and as clients often do, Juan had questions about another horse he had owned. As I wrote out the after care instructions for Cisco, Juan asked me "Do you treat horses with fetlock problems?"

"Well, yes, but there are a lot of problems that occur in the fetlock. Which condition do you mean?"

"I'm not sure. I just had a big, bay gelding that was always sore whenever I rode him. I hadn't met you yet, but I had my other vet out several times. He tried all kinds of things, but nothing worked. He told me it was the fetlock, but we never got him sound."

"You could send him to the veterinary hospital in Fort Collins. They have lameness specialists and their prices are reasonable."

"Really? I heard they were expensive!"

"Well, that's only partly true. Some of the bills seem high, but you need to realize that most of the horses they see have already been treated by local veterinarians, and had problems that were beyond what we can handle. The University can't fix them all, but they have advanced diagnostics, and specialists in surgery and medicine to handle tough cases. They are state supported, and have income from tuition and research grants, and they have the students do much of the work. In my opinion, they perform miracles on a regular basis."

"Gee, I wish I had known that. I gave up on the horse and sold him. He was a really good horse, too!"

"Their bills are less than the cost to replace a good horse. I work with them frequently. If any of your horses have a problem that I can't solve, I'll be glad to put you in touch with a specialist there who can help."

Juan gathered up Cisco's medications, and as he climbed into his pickup he said, "You know...you really *do* know a lot about horses!"

Duh!

"Were you born knowing all this stuff, or did you have to study?"

I closed my eyes in disbelief.

Study?

I studied 16 hours a day for nine years to earn my degree!

"I studied." I said matter-of-factly trying to remain professional.

"See ya later. Thanks Doc."

"You're welcome, Juan."

As I walked back to the house behind Juan's trailer, I thought about my career from Juan's perspective.

After nine years of college, earning a doctorate in veterinary medicine, and 30 years of horse experience *I* certainly thought I knew a lot about horses, but today I realized my training and my diploma don't mean a thing to clients unless I can solve their problems. And I have to earn their respect before they'll even let me try.

Maybe today I won Juan's trust, and now I could make a real difference in the lives of his horses.

Chapter 21 Heartbroken

Around St. Patrick's Day I came home from work to find Patrick down in his stall. He had not colicked for nearly a year, and I had never found him down before I fed him.

I knew he was in trouble.

I got my stethoscope and checked him. His pulse was racing and his gut sounds were too quiet. I feared Patrick would need surgery to survive. I quickly administered pain relievers that were stronger than morphine, struggling to get the medicine into his vein as he staggered around his stall in pain.

I blanketed him against the cold. While the medicine relieved his pain, it wore off in only a few minutes. I administered more pain medicine and did a rectal exam - his intestines were displaced. His only chance at survival was if he had surgery.

As I weighed the option of taking him to surgery, I could see the straps on his blanket grow tighter as his abdomen distended with gas right before my eyes.

Every horse I had referred for colic surgery in the past five years had died on the table, or died within a year of the surgery. I know other vets who reported success stories, but I was not seeing them in my practice.

I remember the horses I cared for when I was a student - horses in the immediate post-op period - how they suffered and lost weight. Poor Patrick was a young horse, but for most of his life he suffered from colic pain.

Patrick's agony returned too quickly, and I dosed him again.

I needed time to think.

Was it humane to put him through more pain, especially if he would only last a year and have more bouts of colic, one of which would eventually kill him? If I knew he would survive surgery and live a long and healthy life, I would send him to surgery in a heartbeat.

But that wasn't likely what Patrick's future would hold.

I couldn't let him suffer any longer. With tears in my eyes I drew up the euthanasia solution and destroyed this lovely, kind horse.

His suffering ended quickly, but so did my hopes for Patrick to have a normal, pain-free life.

I had to know what killed him. Had my management been inadequate? Did Patrick have sand in his intestines - sand that wasn't removed with my treatment? Did he have parasites that were resistant to my dewormers? Did he have intestinal damage from his early years that couldn't heal? Did he have a tumor?

I had to know, but I couldn't bear to cut him open to find out.

Somehow, as hard as it was, in the morning I found the courage to do the post-mortem examination.

I found none of those things in Patrick's abdomen. There was no sand, no tumor, no parasites, and no damaged blood vessels. A part of his large intestine had misplaced itself forward in the abdomen, getting trapped around the base of his stomach. It was one of those things that can happen to any healthy horse.

While Patrick's death tore a hole in my heart, I was glad I gave him a happy year - a year spent eating all day, running in the fields, pestering Rocky, and sunbathing in the sandy paddocks. I had done my best for him, even if that only meant giving him one good year.

I had given him a chance.

I cut a piece of his mane and buried it in the field where he ran in the sunshine.

Chapter 22 Money, Money, Money

The pager went off one summer evening, just as I finished dinner. The answering service told me a neighbor only a few miles away had three horses down with colic. They needed help right away. I got their phone number, and returned the call to Harry and Sally Filbert.

"This is Dr. Thibeault. How can I help you?"

"Dr. Thibeault, this is Sally Filbert. I got your name from Harry's brother Tom. We have three ropin' horses, and none of 'em are eatin' tonight. One's really hurtin', and was down when I got home from the store. My husband Harry is walking 'im right now. Can you come right away?"

"Yes, I can."

I got the Filberts' address and jumped in the truck, with Clancy at my side. The ranch was so close I hardly had time to think about what might be the cause. To have more than one horse fall ill at the same time was unusual. The horses may have been poisoned, or ate poisonous plants growing in the pasture. Something in the feed or water that all three horses consumed was the most likely cause.

I was at the Filberts' ranch before I could come up with a treatment plan.

As I drove in the yard I saw a shiny new Ford pickup in the driveway, and a huge horse trailer sticking out from behind the barn.

"Hello, I'm Dr. Thibeault. How can I help you?"

"Thanks for coming, Doc. I'm Sally Filbert. All three of our ropin' horses have colic. Harry's out back walking Cash. My sons are with him."

"Show me the way," I said as I tossed my stethoscope around my neck and stuffed a thermometer in my pocket.

Sally led me to a dry lot behind the barn.

There were three lean cowboys - lean as bean poles - clad in blue jeans, wide leather belts with big silver buckles, plaid western shirts, and broad brimmed straw hats - typical cowboy summer gear. The tallest cowboy was walking a bay Quarter Horse gelding, whose legs were crumbling under him as he tried to go down. The two shorter cowboys were watching, hands on their hips. The tall cowboy slapped his horse on the shoulder in an effort to keep him on his feet.

Sally introduced me "This is my husband Harry, and my sons Jason and Cody."

Jason looked to be about 16, and Cody was about 12 years old. Their looked like miniature versions of their dad.

Harry said "And this is Cash. Start with him. He's the worst."

Cash threw himself on the ground and began to roll, despite Harry's efforts to keep him up. I could tell from the flattened areas of sand in the paddock that this wasn't the first time he'd been down. He soon got up, and I grabbed my chance to examine him. I listened to his heart. It was racing, indicating that his pain was intense. When I listened to his abdomen, his intestines were rumbling non-stop. His gums were pink, and when I pressed the blood out of his gums with my thumb, they quickly became pink again. As I pinched his skin to test for dehydration, he seemed to relax slightly. That was a good sign. If the pain came and went, he was suffering from intestinal spasms. While spasms are painful, the condition itself was not life-threatening. We just needed to keep him from hurting himself, or us, until the spasms stopped.

"He should be fine. He's just having spasms, and I have treatments to stop them. He'll be feeling better soon."

"Boy, that's a relief. He's my best ropin' horse. I'd hate t' lose him!" said Harry.

I returned to my truck for pain medication, and something to stop the spasms. Trying to hit a vein when the horse is rolling is difficult and dangerous. I waited until Cash was between spasms, so it was easier for me to give the injections.

Whenever I treat a horse for intestinal spasms, I recall my sister's description of the first time she gave birth. She said her response to labor pains was "I'm dying...No, I'm fine...No, I'm dying...No, I'm fine." Apparently equine intestinal spasms and human labor pains are similar in nature.

As the medication eased his pain, Cash soon dropped his head in relaxation. I passed a tube into his stomach to relieve any gas that was causing pressure, and poured mineral oil down the tube to coat his stomach and intestines.

Since Cash was feeling more comfortable now, I went to check the second horse.

Harry and Cody led me into the barn to examine Cody's horse, leaving Jason to watch Cash.

"We call him Silver Dollar, Silver for short."

The gray gelding was standing in the corner of his stall, ignoring the hay in his feeder. While horses with colic don't eat, Silver was having difficulty breathing. When I palpated his throat, he coughed.

"Has he been coughing lately?"

"Now that you mentioned it, he did cough a lot last weekend, when we were at the ropin' in Sterling, but he hasn't coughed as much since we got home."

As I ran my hands over his body, I could tell Silver had a fever. I inserted my thermometer into his rectum. I listened to his chest, and could hear fluid sounds, instead of the soft sounds of air moving. Silver had pneumonia. The thermometer confirmed it - a fever of 103.4.

"What has Silver been vaccinated against?"

Sally spoke up "Well, you know, we usually use ol' Doc Hastings, but he just doesn't understand how valuable these horses are to us. I think he likes working on cattle better than horses. He just comes out in the spring and gives 'em some vaccinations, and that's it. I really don't know what they've had. We need to find a vet that understands how valuable these horses are to us, and that can keep 'em healthy."

Harry added "Did you see the new truck in the driveway? We won that ropin'. We need our horses healthy. Our horses mean the world to us."

Horses that are used for competitions are stressed by long trailer rides, strenuous exercise, lack of sleep while traveling, changes in diet, and exposure to illnesses when they mingle with horses from all over the country. It is difficult to keep them competing at their best, but a good preventative medical program can help.

Horses that get pneumonia usually get one of the common viral respiratory infections first. While there's no specific treatment against the virus, there are vaccines to prevent the infections. And a healthy horse that is allowed to rest will usually recover from the viral infection on its own. However, if the horse is stressed by exercise or trailering, it may end up with a secondary bacterial infection that settles in its lungs, causing pneumonia. Pneumonia is very serious and may be fatal. Silver had probably not been vaccinated, and I knew he was ridden hard, and trailered several hundred miles. Obviously the Filberts had not noticed he was sick, so he had all the factors that lead to complications from pneumonia.

Rest and fresh air are important aspects in the treatment of respiratory infections, and antibiotics can help clear the bacterial part of the infection. Knowledgeable owners can prevent these complications by vaccinating their horses on schedule, and noticing when they are sick so they don't stress them further. The Filberts did neither of these things to help Silver. Either Dr. Hastings didn't spend the time to educate the Filberts about equine health care, or the Filberts didn't listen. I would be glad to help the Filberts keep Silver from getting sick again - if I could cure him first.

"I'll be glad to set up a vaccination, deworming, and preventative health care program for all of your horses, once we get them well. Silver needs to be rested for at least a month. Keep him home - no trailer rides anywhere. He's very sick, and any more stress could kill him. I'll give him antibiotics, and we'll begin a course of vaccinations once he recovers."

As I walked to my truck to get the medications for Silver, I saw that Cash had begun nibbling at his hay.

"Well, Doc, he looks like he's feeling better."

"Yes, he does."

It was such a shame that Silver was so sick, when a simple, inexpensive vaccination could have kept him healthy. Cash probably was full of sand, since the Filberts threw his hay on the sandy ground. His deworming program was probably inadequate, too. If I could improve the Filberts' management practices - get them on a serious deworming program, have them use hay mangers, and treat the horses for sand - maybe Cash wouldn't colic again either.

I returned to the barn and began Silver's treatment with penicillin, and an anti-inflammatory medication to lower his fever and make him feel better. He had a better chance of fighting the infection if I could get him eating and drinking as soon as possible. Dehydration depresses the immune system, and Silver was already slightly dehydrated. He may be unable to fight off the infection.

I was finished with Silver.

"Where's the third horse?"

"Jason's horse, Penny, is in the back barn." Harry and Jason took me to a cramped, wooden barn at the back of Cash's paddock. The air was hot and stagnant, as the small window wasn't open.

As Jason slipped a halter on the sorrel gelding, Harry told me "Penny coughs and has a runny nose sometimes, but today he's not eating, so he's colicking too," said Harry.

I was beginning to think that colic was the only disease the Filberts knew. For a family that depends on their horses for income, I was surprised how ignorant they were about their horses. With books, videos, magazines, and seminars, most people become educated after a few years of horse ownership.

But not the Filberts!

Penny was also having breathing problems. He had difficulty moving the air out of his lungs, in a respiratory movement called a double expiratory lift. When he breathed out, the air would not flow normally out of his lungs, so he had to push with his abdominal muscles to move the stale air out. The extra effort made his abdominal muscles enlarge, so a visible line could be seen along his belly. This extra effort to breathe was tiring, and would get worse over time.

Penny wasn't hot to the touch, but I inserted a thermometer to check for a fever. While waiting, I listened to his chest, and heard the squeaks and wheezes characteristic of a horse suffering from heaves. His temperature was normal, as I had expected.

"Penny is broken winded - a condition also called heaves. He is allergic to something in his environment, and has damaged his lungs so they don't expel air normally. There is not much I can do to help him, but there is a lot you can do, Harry.

"I'll get this bout under control with some medications, but they have complications if given for a long time. In ten days he should be feeling better, and if you follow my guidelines, he should do better in the future.

"First of all, move him out of the barn. Even though there's no grass on your ranch, put him in a paddock outside with just a loafing shed. That should protect him from the wind, but still give him plenty of fresh air. Feed him the cleanest hay you can find, and wet it down if he coughs when he eats. If he still coughs, you'll have to switch him over to pellets.

"Can we still rope on him? He's always been a great rope horse," Jason wanted to know.

"Well, that's hard to say. The medications will get him turned around, and your management changes can decrease his coughing and wheezing, but I can't cure heaves. If you rope outside, avoiding indoor arenas, and if the arena is watered down to decrease dust, he'll do better. How much better? I can't say. We'll just have to wait and see.

"If he gets an infection, he'll really get sick, so vaccinations are even more important for him than for your other horses. We have to wait a couple of weeks until he feels better, and after the medication is out of his system we can vaccinate him. The medication will interfere with the vaccine."

I went to my truck and got some antihistamines, steroids, and antibiotics for Penny. That was the best treatment available at the time. Penny would need the Filberts to change their management if he was going to get any better.

I treated Penny, and by now Cash was looking normal. I followed Sally to the house to figure up the bill. As I worked on it, the Filberts questioned me about preventive medicine.

"We really don't want to miss so much competition because our horses are sick. We need 'em performin' at their best. Doc

Hastings doesn't talk much 'bout prevention. We can see you're real thorough. Will you do our vet work from now on?"

"Yes. I'd be glad to. Here's what I would do for your horses, because they are competitive athletes."

"First - deworm them every six weeks. Vaccinate every spring against tetanus and encephalitis, twice a year against strangles, and four times a year against flu and Rhino.

"Put your hay in feeders and put rubber mats below the feeders so the horses don't eat sand when they are nibbling up the scraps. And feed them psyllium ten days a month to remove sand that gets into their intestines, because your farm is as sandy as mine."

"Well…that all sounds pretty expensive!"

"This is exactly the same program I use on my own horses, and I think your horses would be much healthier if you made these management changes.

"And if you'd take the extra step to check their temperatures every morning when you're traveling, then you'd know if one of them was coming down with something. You could get it treated early before it became so serious. You wouldn't risk having your horses die from pneumonia. That's free, and only takes a few minutes. It can save you money in the long run."

"Well, we're not made of money, you know. How much is all this gonna cost?" asked Sally.

"A lot less than a new pick-up!"

"Well…can we save some money by bringing the horses to your clinic?" asked Jason.

"Yes, you will save the trip charge."

"And can we buy the vaccines at the feed store and give them ourselves?" asked Harry.

"Yes, Harry, you can, but most feed stores don't carry the best brands, because careful manufacturers don't let their vaccines get into the hands of untrained people. When vaccines are shipped to feed stores and tack shops, the box may sit overnight before it's unloaded, and vaccines must be kept cool. I know, because I worked for six years at a tack store that sold medications, and they weren't always handled properly. And unless you take a cooler of ice with you to the store, the vaccines will get warm in the pick-up on the way home.

"Sally, if you want the best care for your horses, find a veterinarian you can trust, and follow his or her advice. If you don't trust me, pick somebody else, because veterinarians are the best source of the information you need to keep your horses healthy. It's a lot cheaper to prevent disease than to treat it. In human medicine, they know that every dollar spent on preventive medicine saves ten dollars in treatment costs. After all, that is what you want, isn't it?"

"Well…yeah."

I handed Sally the bill for today's services.

"Call me in two weeks if you want to get your horses on the road to good health. I'll be glad to help you, if you'll let me."

As I drove home, I wondered how I could be so lucky as to have found another family of Filberts.

But most of all, I felt sorry for their horses.

Chapter 23 Quaking Like an Aspen

"Hi Marcia, it's Paige. Do you have a minute?"

"Sure Paige, what's up?"

I recognized Dr. Garnett's distinctive voice. We had been classmates in vet school.

"Well, I know you found a good home for Boo, and I have another Border collie in trouble. I thought maybe you could help. She needs someone who understands Border collies."

Dr. Garnett related Emily's sad tale. She was in a loving family, but due to allergies the children developed to her, the dog was relegated to living in the back yard. Emily would sit on the picnic table looking through the window at the family inside, isolated from their companionship. With six kids she had plenty to watch, but little to do.

She was boundary trained, and would not leave the yard, but was terrified of neighborhood children when they came into the yard to play.

Some dogs are very shy, and if they can't escape when someone threatening enters their personal space they may bite out of fear. But fear biters can be as dangerous as aggressive dogs, if they cannot overcome their fear.

"She's afraid, not aggressive," Dr. Garnett informed me.

"Does she get enough exercise?"

Border collies need a lot of exercise. They were bred to work for shepherds on the farm, herding their flocks into the barn every night. If they live in town they need long walks or games of fetch to satisfy their need for exercise. These intelligent, energetic dogs develop vices that drive their owners crazy if they are deprived of adequate exercise.

"Well, sort of…"

"What does that mean?"

"Their uncle has a farm, and they thought Emily would love to run out there, but it's a two hour drive, and Emily gets carsick. I think it's a fear issue again, but the family told me when they took her to the farm the first time they thought she would rather die than get in the car to come home. She quaked like an aspen leaf on a windy fall day."

Paige went on, "And one more thing. She tows their daughter around the neighborhood on roller blades."

"Did they use a special harness for that, or just her collar and leash?"

"No, unfortunately they used her collar."

Once dogs learn to pull against the leash, it's harder to teach them to walk quietly at your side.

"Great! So I take it she hasn't been to obedience school."

"No."

"How is she around other dogs?"

"I think she's too afraid to bother Clancy."

"Well, let's hope so. Clancy went through enough with Boo. It sounds like there's plenty to work on."

"So, you'll take her?"

"I'd like to meet her first, but you know I'm a sucker for a sob story."

"Yeah, I know."

I made arrangements with Dr. Garnett to have Emily brought into her clinic later that week.

Paige called me when Emily arrived, so I drove to Paige's clinic after I finished my day's rounds.

"Hi, Paige. How's she doing?"

"She's scared to death to be left here, poor girl, but I think it's the best thing for her. You'll have your hands full with her, Marcia, but she's so sweet. I'll get her. Meet me in the first exam room."

I went in and Paige soon brought Emily on a leash, slinking into the exam room. Paige had to restrain her in order to close the door, as Emily wanted nothing to do with us, or the exam room.

Emily was much smaller than Clancy. She was so afraid she practically dragged her belly on the ground, and wouldn't make eye contact. I sat down on the floor to be less imposing, but she wouldn't come near, just keeping her face to the door and trying to get out, away from us.

"She's a shy girl, isn't she?" I asked softly.

"Yeah, she is. I don't know if you want to take her on, but she really needs someone who understands Border collies to give her another chance."

I sat there for a few minutes, talking quietly to Paige and ignoring Emily. I did not approach her, and she showed no desire to bite. She seemed submissive and gentle, not dangerous. She gradually glanced in my direction, although clearly I was too formidable to look at directly. Paige and I continued talking. Emily relaxed a bit, and as we ignored her, she started to steal glances at me. In time, she walked softly around the room, and finally came over to sniff my knee.

"My jeans carry the scents of all of the animals I treated today, don't they girl? I'll bet you can pick out each one, can't you?" I whispered to her without moving or looking at her.

I sat very still and kept my eyes down. In time she came close enough that I could pat her, and I was glad to see she didn't pull away when I moved my hand towards her. She seemed to relax when I touched her, but it was hard not to look at her.

"Well, Paige, I'm willing to give her a try, but I can't guarantee how things will go. Boo and Clancy never could work things out, but Boo wound up with a good home anyway. I'll do my best. And who knows, Clancy may even like her!"

"Oh Marcia, I'm sure you'll do fine. Thanks for your help."

"I brought the farm truck with the camper shell. It has rubber mats for traction and it will be safe for her. I brought Clancy along to keep her company, but I think I'll keep Clancy up front with me because Emily's so shy. They can meet each other through the window. I'll keep them separated until I know Emily a little better."

I gently picked up Emily, who stiffened up her entire body, and became a quivering canine board.

"Sorry girl. You hardly know me, and I'm gonna put you in the truck, and I know you'll hate it. But we have to get you home, and it's way too far to walk." I apologized as I carried her to my truck."

Dr. Garnett opened the tail gate and I put Emily inside. As I closed the tailgate I felt so sorry for her. She was splay-legged in fear, stiff and trembling. I had never seen a dog so afraid of a truck. I wondered what had happened to her to trigger so much fear. She was drooling on her front paws. Poor thing. How I wished animals could understand a human's reassuring words! It would make things so much easier.

I said goodbye to Paige and climbed in the front of the truck to a warm greeting from Clancy. She was always so glad to see me. Hopefully someday Emily would greet people with such joy.

"Hey, Clancy. You're getting a new playmate. Hopefully this one won't terrorize you like Boo did."

Clancy spent the trip home staring through the rear window at Emily. Emily spent the whole trip in the spot where I put her, staring out the back of the truck, rigid and too terrified to move. She drooled a lake of saliva beneath her paws.

I wished I had another way to get her home, but I didn't. Hopefully I could teach her that going in the car was a fun thing. Or maybe Clancy could teach her. Clancy loved going in the car and enthusiasm can be contagious. Boo had learned how to get along with dogs from other dogs. Clancy's friendly, outgoing personality might make her a good role model for Emily.

When we got home I let Clancy run in the farmyard, but snapped a leash on Emily before I opened the tailgate. I had to make sure she couldn't run off.

"Come on girl. You'll like it here. I promise," I said as I lifted her rigid body to the ground. It was a good thing I had put the leash on her, as she bolted, trying to get away.

"Come on, girl. With me."

As I got to the back door Dr. Mom was waiting for us.

"So this is Emily."

Emily strained against the leash, trying to avoid going into the house.

"Yes. She's so sweet, but so scared. Mom, I'll turn her loose on the screened porch and just let her come to you on her own terms. She's afraid of eye contact, so if you don't look at her, she'll be less afraid."

"I'll go get some brushes. Maybe she'd like a little grooming." she said quietly.

"Okay, but take it slowly."

Dr. Mom got Clancy's brushes and sat down on the carpeted floor.

Emily looked out the glass door, wishing she could escape. I sat on the floor next to Dr. Mom, quietly talking about Emily and how to help her. As time passed, Emily began exploring the porch, keeping her back to us, avoiding eye contact. Eventually she came close enough to sniff Mom's leg. However, if either of us looked directly at her, she would back off. In only a few minutes she came up and sniffed Dr. Mom's hand, so she reached out and stroked Emily. We avoided eye contact and she was getting more comfortable. Soon Emily was lying down next to Dr. Mom's leg, and Mom picked up a soft brush and began brushing her back gently, with long strokes. We both kept our voices down and our demeanor quiet. As Dr. Mom brushed, Emily's eyes began to close. I am sure she was exhausted after her terrifying truck ride. She was lonely for companionship and was really enjoying the caresses. Slowly she rolled over onto her back and let Mom brush her stomach. Dr. Mom stayed with her for over an hour, stroking and bonding to her.

As evening approached, I got up to feed the horses. Without moving, Emily opened one eye as if to say "Go on without me. I'll call you if I need anything."

As I walked down to the barn, I was glad Paige had called me. Emily was a lovely dog, and she certainly deserved another chance. With Dr. Mom's help Emily got off to a great start. They were soon bonded.

The next day I took Emily down to the barn on a leash while I fed the horses. Her leash manners were terrible. She pulled so hard I got a rope burn on my hand. I occasionally got rope burns when handling horses, but I didn't think that was possible from a 27 pound dog. She was excited and barked at the horses, but I knew this was a new experience for her, so I was patient.

When I fed the dogs, I put Emily on the porch and Clancy in the kitchen to avoid any fighting. As soon as Emily finished eating, before I could pick up the empty bowls, she did her business on the rug. Hmpph. I thought she was supposed to be housebroken. Didn't she live in the house until the children developed allergies? It looked like I had another problem to fix.

I decided to stand by Emily at each feeding, and take her outside as soon as she finished. This helped, although housebreaking her would be no easy task.

Emily's behavior when she was loose in the house was atrocious. The first time I brought her in, I sat in my easy chair, trying to exude an aura of calm. Animals often respond to the emotions of people and animals around them, and I hoped if she saw me calm, it would calm her. Clancy slept in her favorite spot under the table while Emily explored her new surroundings rather exuberantly. She ran around like a cougar had her by the tail. As I leaned forward in my chair to grab the newspaper, Emily leapt over the table, ran across the sofa, and jumped over my back, bouncing off the back of my chair and onto the floor again. At that point I decided Emily would wear a leash around the house for a few weeks until she calmed down.

While Clancy and Dr. Mom went on calls with me every day, I left Emily home with Dad. She would need my undivided attention in the truck until she could overcome her fear. Dad pretended not to like dogs, but one day I came home from work and caught Emily sleeping in Dad's lap while he sat in his easy chair. He was really a softie.

After each day's calls, I worked on Emily's fear of riding in trucks. I pulled my vet truck up alongside the house, and invited Emily to get in. She declined, pinning herself tightly against the ground. I spoke to her softly as I gently picked her up and put her on the front seat. She immediately slithered to the floor and got into her splay-legged position, with her head down and drooling. I started the engine, drove 100 feet to the garage, parked, and let her out. She was elated to be out so soon. I repeated this exercise a few times each day for a week, and Emily seemed much less fearful. Finally one day she stayed crouched on the seat without seeking refuge on the floor. I knew she would be okay the day she showed the courage to sit up on the seat and look out the window.

Now I could take Emily on short trips off the farm. I would take her when I went to town for errands. I took Clancy along to keep Emily company. Clancy slept when I drove, only raising her head when I used the turn signals. If she could tell we were going someplace fun, like to Mary Wilkinson's or Larry Whitley's, she'd get up. Otherwise, she'd just plop back down on the seat and resume her nap. Maybe Emily could adopt Clancy's attitude towards truck rides.

I often left the truck windows down when I was at an appointment, because I wanted to keep the truck cool for Clancy, and she knew not to jump out. She didn't seem to mind staying in the truck as much if she knew she could get out at will, rather than being held in by closed doors and windows. In fact, when I closed the windows, Clancy'd become more agitated than if I left them open. When I was working on a patient, she would sit quietly in the truck, keeping an eye on me, ready to help at a moment's notice.

However, if I was shopping in town or eating at a restaurant, I always locked the truck to keep my medical equipment safe, providing bowls of ice water for cooling and only cracking the windows to let the heat escape. I did not realize, however, how fiercely Clancy guarded the truck when I was out of sight, until one day, when I was coming back to the truck after picking up groceries. Clancy usually focused on me until I entered the store, stared at the door until I reappeared, and then wagged her tail until I was back safely in the truck. But this day Clancy did not see me coming. She was focused on an elderly lady pushing her grocery cart to her car, which was parked next to mine. Clancy waited until the lady was right alongside my truck, putting her key into her door, when Clancy let loose with the most blood curdling barking tirade I'd ever heard from her. I thought the lady was going to have a heart attack on the spot. I scolded Clancy and apologized to the lady, although I don't know that the apology was accepted. I soon learned that this was one of Clancy's habits, and for some reason she seemed to prefer senior citizens. I soon began parking further back on the lot, away from where the seniors chose to park. She never barked at anyone if Dr. Mom was in the car or I was in sight.

One day, when Emily was not with me, I stopped for a late lunch at a fast food restaurant. It was a hot summer afternoon, and there were no other cars on the parking lot. I was just going to hurry in and order food, choosing not to use the drive-through because I needed to wash up after my morning's appointments. I left the windows down in the truck so Clancy would be comfortable. I knew Clancy could see me inside except when I was washing up, and I would only be gone a few minutes anyway. As I came out of the washroom, I saw to my horror a local farm worker standing at the counter, looking flushed and angry. I'm not that fluent in Spanish, especially the words he chose that day, but by his gestures I understood that when he got out of his truck, which he parked right next to mine, Clancy apparently went into her barking tirade right in his face, hanging out the window by her toenails. I disavowed any support of her activities, but had a talk with her later. She'd never done that before - she usually just wagged her tail and begged for attention when the window was open - and I never saw her do it again. I decided the drive-thru might be a better option in the future, and made certain Emily didn't pick up this behavior from Clancy.

In a few short weeks Emily demonstrated emphatically that her fear of car rides was over. She had been running in the back yard when I invited her to join me for a Sunday ride to town. When I opened the truck door she came streaking across the yard and with a flying leap, landed in her seat in the truck. She proudly sat up, looking around from her high perch. It was a good day!

I was still working on Emily's fear of strangers.

Many people love dogs, but when they see one they approach the dog with their heads down in the dog's face, staring into the dog's eyes. This is okay for most friendly dogs, but Emily was unnerved by such behavior. Dogs, especially Border collies that herd sheep by driving them with eye contact, are very sensitive to this form of communication. Sheep dogs that are tough enough to herd cattle are said to have a 'strong eye.' They use this eye contact to communicate with each other, and Emily was a dog that submitted to strong eye contact, but was also terrorized by it.

I hoped Emily would overcome her fear of people if she could be introduced to enough kind strangers. My practice is filled with animal lovers, so if I could get them to help, she would progress rapidly. I needed to get them not to look at her, but I had to be careful. People sometimes become offended if their behavior is criticized. Training must be pleasant for both my clients and Emily.

So I made training Emily a game, and invited clients to play. I would keep Emily in another room until I could ask "Would you help me train my dog?" People are usually willing to help when asked, and no one refused. When they replied "Sure, what do you want me to do?" it opened the door for me to explain Emily's rules of social conduct.

"It's so simple. Just come on my porch and ignore my new dog. Don't talk to her. Especially don't look at her. Don't touch her until she touches you, and don't look at her even then."

Dave Fletcher was the first to agree to help. He stood on the back porch and we talked about his horses. Emily at first backed away, then came up behind Dave and sniffed the back of his knee. Border collies know which direction a person is facing, always bringing the sheep to the shepherd's front side. By approaching strangers from behind, she could avoid eye contact. In a few minutes she licked Dave's hand, and he stroked her. Once contact was established, Dave could reach out and pat her and she wouldn't run away. We could then glance at her, but Dave kindly avoided staring.

I repeated this exercise with dozens of clients, and soon Emily was ready to greet clients as I made my farm rounds. We did this exercise at clients' farms as well. She began greeting clients with joyous enthusiasm. As time went on, she met so many people that she began to greet strangers as old friends, rather than as threats, and before my eyes this shy, fearful dog grew happy and confident.

However, a new problem developed. Emily grew protective of my truck. Like Clancy, Emily was content to stay in the truck with the windows open while I treated my patients. She and Clancy got along fine. At the end of each farm call, I would climb back into my truck and fill out the medical records, giving the owner after-care instructions, and handing the clients a bill for the day's services. Emily would be in the back seat behind me and would stick her nose out the front window under my shoulder belt. As clients were paying their bills by passing a check through the window, Emily started growling at them.

I had to chastise her, "Not now, Emily! This is where the dog food money comes from!"

I convinced her that protecting the truck was not necessary, so she let down her guard when I was around to protect the truck myself.

I could not get Emily housebroken, and her leash manners made it dangerous for Dr. Mom to handle her if I was away. So Emily went back to live with her original family, who always loved her.

Emily enjoys rides in the truck, so she goes to the family farm where she runs to her heart's content. Having lost her fear of strangers, she now plays happily with the family's friends in the yard.

The family cried when they had to give her up, and they cried in happiness when they got her back.

They now understood how to help her.

Chapter 24 Any Way I Can

Sometimes I wonder how I get myself into these things - bouncing on the back of a motorcycle down a rough, mountain trail, optimistic I was carrying all the supplies I would need to treat a horse with colic.

I had been working at the Rocky Creek veterinary checkpoint, waiting for more riders at the 75 mile inspection for the Annual Spring Fling endurance race, when Jessie came galloping in on Albert, shouting that there was a horse in trouble on the trail.

"Pat Deems' horse Whizzer is down a few miles out, and he looks like he's got colic! I told him I'd get here as soon as I could. Please help him." Jessie jumped off Albert and began cooling him down. Her pit crew came to help her.

Luckily there were two vets at the checkpoint, so one of us could leave. I volunteered. Dr. Small had flown in from out of state to help with the judging. Since I was local, I brought my vet truck, fully stocked with everything I was likely to need.

Ty, Betty Carlow's wrangler that had offered Boo a good home, had his motorcycle at the checkpoint. It came in handy during emergencies and when riders were lost on the trail, so he offered me a ride. He knew the trails like the back of his hand and his experience with horses would be welcome if I needed help.

The trail was too narrow for a truck, and the horse was too far away to get there quickly on foot. Ty's motorcycle would be the fastest way.

I grabbed my steel bucket, gallon of mineral oil, stomach pump, stomach tube, stethoscope, needles, syringes, bags of IV fluids, a catheter, IV lines and medicines. I hoped that was everything I'd need. I put what I could in the bucket and stuffed the small things in my jacket pockets. The fluids wouldn't fit anywhere else, so I stuffed them inside my jacket until I looked like I'd gained 100 pounds. I wondered what Spirit's owner, Vince Carson, would say if he could see me now.

I climbed on the motorcycle behind Ty. The heavy bucket and bags of fluids were awkward enough, not to mention the trail was meant for horses' hooves, not wheels. My arms were so full I couldn't hold on to Ty. Rats!

As we went down the trail, swerving around rocks and bumping over tree roots, I was thinking about the problem I faced. Perhaps it wasn't colic at all and the horse was tied up with severe muscle cramps, or had an injury. I could carry only a fraction of the supplies my truck held. There was no way to get everything to Pat's horse. I had to trust Jessie. She was becoming well-informed about endurance riding, and Pat Deems was experienced. Colic was common in endurance riding. I hoped I had chosen wisely.

For some reason it glanced across my mind that maybe medical school would have been a better option for me than veterinary school. ER docs get to stand in well-equipped emergency rooms, with residents and nurses and the latest equipment at hand to help them treat their patients. I didn't have the advantage of high-tech equipment, but rather have to rely on my quick thinking and ability to improvise when I work "in the field."

No, the thought raced on through. Human medicine was definitely not my choice. I was doing what I loved. I loved the horses and their owners, and the camaraderie amongst veterinarians. My colleagues and I studied hard and worked incredibly long hours, for a small fraction of what we'd be paid if we were physicians. But the passion for veterinary practice and dedication to relieving animal suffering kept us going. The fresh scent of the pine forest as we climbed the ridge made my office the most beautiful office I could imagine.

Holding on tightly onto my jostling supplies, I recalled how well Whizzer looked earlier in the race.

More Horse Calls

I had been assigned to Pine Meadow checkpoint, and got there just after sunrise, after overseeing the last horses get on the trail from the starting line at base camp. The first two 100 milers, Pat and Terry Deems, were trotting into Pine Meadow as I arrived. The heat was rising off the backs of their horses as they came down into the cool valley, still dark in the shadow of the mountain. The steep terrain would keep the sun at bay a while longer.

Pine Meadow was the first checkpoint for the 100 milers. The two horses in the lead were really flying, as I was 20 minutes ahead of their projected arrival time and they were already here. Dr. Small and I briefly exchanged greetings, and went to work examining the horses. He had already paced out the distance for the Ridgway index, where we would trot the horses for their metabolic evaluations.

The noted endurance veterinarian, Dr. Kerry Ridgway, had determined a more accurate assessment of stress than simply taking a horse's resting heart rate after a period of exercise. He found that if a horse had a brief rest after a bout of exercise, and then was asked to jog a short, prescribed distance, the horse's heart rate after the short exercise more accurately reflected the horse's cardiovascular fitness. This test worked well, so I used it for every race now.

Dr. Small had chosen the access road for the trot out. Its firm surface would enhance most lameness problems, so we could evaluate fatigue and lameness at the same time. There shouldn't be any trucks on the road, as the pit crews were already in place, spread out across the meadow, ready to help the horse and rider teams as they came in. It was always congested around the water, but pit crews had arrived early and filled buckets from the creek. They would water the horses and sponge off the sweat, while the riders got drinks and food. The horses could replenish their energy from the mountain grasses, and the pit crews mixed up concoctions for the horses to replace lost electrolytes. The riders would get fruit and energy bars from their pit crews.

At Pine Meadows Pat had brought his bay gelding, Whizzer, to me while his wife took her mare, Firefly, to Dr. Small. It seemed odd that Pat had a pit crew member with him, because Whizzer seemed okay, but then I noticed Pat was limping badly.

"Hi. Pat. How's it going?"

"This young horse is doing great! He's so competitive. I can hardly slow him down. He's not that fit because I haven't had him long and it's so early in the season. There's still so much snow at my ranch I haven't been able to do all the training runs I'd like. I'm going to pull him at the halfway point. We're really just here pacing my wife's horse. She's gonna win."

"You sound confident!"

"I am! You just watch. She'll win."

"Well, it's a good thing you don't have to pass the vet check. You aren't very sound yourself. What happened to you?"

"Yeah, it *is* a good thing the riders don't have to pass the vet inspection, isn't it! I broke my leg last month, so I brought a pinch runner."

"How'd you break your leg?"

"One of my Hereford cows charged me as I was closing a gate and smashed my leg right into the gate. The doctor put a cast on it, but when I tried to ride my young colt the cast got to swinging and thumped him on the side, and I got bucked off. I can't ride with it, so I figure I'm better off without it, so I took it off last week. It's nearly healed, and I'll be good as new soon."

"Did you consider not riding until you were healed?"

"No."

What was he thinking?

"Okay, let's check that pony."

Pat held Whizzer's lead while I listened to the gelding's heart, lungs and gut sounds. Pat had pulled his saddle, and sponged off Whizzer's back so I could check for saddle sores. Whizzer looked fit to go on. Then Pat handed the lead over to his helper for the jogging portion of the exam. Whizzer trotted out soundly, his limber legs moving rhythmically and freely. When I listened to the colt's heart after the exercise, his heart rate was slow and steady. He was working well within his limits.

"You're free to go, Pat, but take care of yourself out there."

"Will do."

Firefly passed Dr. Small's exam, and soon Pat and Terry were riding out of the checkpoint. Terry and Firefly would eventually win the race, just as Pat had predicted.

But I wondered what had happened to Pat and Whizzer since then.

The motorcycle ride seemed to take forever - the sick horse was several miles down the trail. As we crested the last ridge, I was glad to see Whizzer standing and grazing in the meadow alongside the trail. Pat had pulled his saddle off.

Ty stopped the motorcycle and held it steady while I climbed off clumsily.

"Thanks, Ty."

"Welcome."

"Boy, are we glad to see you, Doc."

"Hi, Pat. What's with Whizzer?"

"I planned to pull him at 50 miles, but he felt so good, and Dr. Brown said he was doing fine, so I decided to let him go on, although Terry went ahead because she had the better horse. A few miles out of the last vet check he stopped a couple of times, so I slowed to a walk. I don't know if he's cramping or if it's colic, but he seems a lot better since I stopped."

Whizzer looked pretty good. He was covered with dried sweat, which is typical of endurance horses working hard in the mountains. But Pat was a good horseman, and always gave his horses water at every opportunity. When I pinched a fold of skin on Whizzer's neck it snapped back quickly, so Whizzer wasn't too dehydrated. His pulse was slightly elevated, but I considered it normal in light of the exercise he had been doing. His gut sounds were noticeably decreased. That could be from exertion, from colic, or from pain. I ran my hands over all of his major muscles on the back, hip and shoulder. If he had tied up his cramping muscles would feel as hard as stone, but his muscles were supple and soft.

"Pat, he's definitely not tied up."

"Well, I don't understand it. I feel like a fool crying wolf. He seemed sick, and now he seems fine."

"Don't feel foolish, Pat. This is fairly common in endurance horses. It's called exhaustion colic. Whizzer burned his blood sugar while running, and lost fluids and electrolytes through his sweat. Because he's not very fit yet, his fluid and electrolytes got out of balance. When that happened, he couldn't go on. But after he stopped, the blood flow shifted from his muscles to his digestive tract, so he absorbed the fluid and nutrients in his gut. There's a huge reservoir the horse can use to replenish his blood. So, you did exactly the right thing. By stopping him, you reduced the muscle's demand for blood, and allowed Whizzer to heal himself."

"So it's sort of like not swimming after you eat?"

"Yes! Humans and horses only have enough blood flow to support strenuous exercise or digestion. As he gets fitter he'll be able to handle exercise more easily."

I rechecked Whizzer and his vital signs were improving.

"I'd just stay here for a while longer. Let him eat and drink. We'll go back to camp and radio for someone from your pit crew to bring you a fresh horse to ride out, since you're too lame to walk, and someone can lead Whizzer to the nearest road to trailer him to base camp. Even though he looks fine now, I wouldn't suggest riding him out."

I climbed on the motorcycle behind Ty for another bouncy, bone-jarring ride back to the vet check. Since Whizzer needed no treatment, my arms were still aching with a full load of supplies on the return trip. Ty's noisy, exhaust-belching two-wheeled steed certainly couldn't float above the rocky paths with the smooth grace of the beautiful Arabian horses traversing the trails today. But, as rough and noisy as my mount was, it sure beat walking.

That fact that horses can recover, if people recognize the problem early, amazes me. Whizzer would be okay. I didn't want Pat to feel foolish - I wanted him to understand how to protect Whizzer.

When I got back to Rocky Creek there was a long line of horses waiting to be checked. I dropped the supplies in the grass and got my battered body on its feet, calling for the next rider in line.

Chapter 25 No Money - No Change

I was a bit surprised when the Filberts actually called me shortly after I treated Cash, Silver and Penny, to schedule an appointment for vaccinations. Maybe they really did care more for their horses than for their money.

But they wanted to save the trip charge, so I made an appointment to meet Jason at my clinic.

My Dad hoped I'd outfit my clinic with the latest technology, thinking I should pour my money into fancy equipment. But I knew my cost-conscious clients would haul their horses in primarily to save the expense of the farm call.

 The main function of my clinic would be as a classroom for educational seminars. Educating owners was the best way to improve the health of my patients.

Jason Filbert arrived a few minutes late. I met him on the parking lot, as my clinic was now still a few days from completion.

When he unloaded the trailer, I saw he only had one horse with him - Silver.

"Where are Penny and Cash?"

"Well, my dad and I talked it over and we decided to try your program on one horse, and see if it works. We're not rich, you know. And we want to give the flu vaccines ourselves, because they're cheaper at the feed store."

I wondered how he knew it was cheaper, since he never asked me what I charged.

"And we've heard that the Strep vaccine is dangerous. Our friends told us not to use it. All I want today is the rhino shot 'cause the feed store don't carry it."

I could see the Filberts sought a second opinion about vaccinations from their roping buddy, and trusted it more than they trusted my opinion.

"Well Jason, you need to decide who you want to care for your horses, your buddies, or a veterinarian. You've been relying on yourselves, your neighbors and your friends for advice, and last month I was at your ranch treating all three of your horses because they were sick! How's that working for you so far?"

"Uh…"

"I've seen horses die of Strep infections, and I treat many seriously ill horses because their owners didn't vaccinate them."

I pointed to Rocky standing in a nearby paddock -1500 pounds of well-muscled Quarter Horse, whose short, sleek summer coat looked like it was spray painted on. He was the absolute picture of a healthy horse.

"See that buckskin gelding in the first paddock? He's gotten the vaccine twice a year since I bought him. Do you think I'd put my own horse in danger? I give the vaccine to him because I want him to stay healthy. Does he look healthy to you?"

"Well…yeah."

"I've used over a thousand doses, and see a lot fewer sick horses than I used to before this vaccine was available. Not one of those thousand doses resulted in a serious problem, but it's your call. Silver's your horse."

"Well…I just want you to give the Rhino shot. I'm not gonna let you give the Strep vaccine, and I'll give the flu shot myself."

"Okay, fine."

I was so angry, because I knew the Filberts' horses would be sick again soon. They mingled with other horses at rodeos, and were stressed by the long trailer rides, but what could I do?

I administered the vaccine to Silver.

"Be sure and bring him back in three weeks for a booster. Since he hasn't had this vaccine before, he'll need boosters to protect him."

"Okay."

I handed him a bill for $12, which he paid. The price hardly covered the time I spent waiting for Jason to come.

I tried to compose myself. I could help the Filberts' horses, if only they'd let me.

"Jason, I really don't think we've made a difference in the health of your horses today. If you're serious about having your horses competing at their best, you should re-consider your decisions. Your mom complained that Dr. Hastings didn't realize how valuable your horses were - that your horses had won a truck for you, worth thousands of dollars. But it seems that you are the ones who are not willing to treat these horses as if they are valuable."

"I'll think about it," said Jason sullenly, as he loaded Silver into the trailer.

As he drove out I was disappointed that these talented horses did not have caring owners. The Filberts claimed they wanted to keep their horses healthy, and blamed Dr. Hastings when they got sick. He probably tried as hard as I did to help them.

As Jason drove out, I thought they'd probably blame me for any future problems, ignoring the good advice I gave them, like they blamed Dr. Hastings.

It wasn't long before I heard from the Filberts again.

"This is Jason Filbert. Silver is sick. Can I bring him right over?"

"Yes, I'll be here."

This time Jason arrived with his little brother, Cody, and his mother.

I examined Silver, and found he had a fever and a cough. Clearly he was fighting a respiratory infection. Luckily, it had not yet developed into pneumonia, so with rest he would fight off the infection on his own.

"When did you give him the flu vaccination?" I asked Jason.

Mrs. Filbert jumped in between Jason and me, sticking her face in mine and shouting, "We paid *you* to do that!"

As the hackles went up on my neck, I stood tall and looked Mrs. Filbert right in the eye.

"No, you didn't. When Jason arrived, he refused to let me vaccinate Silver for Strep, and said that he'd get the flu vaccine at the feed store to save money. He only let me vaccinate Silver against Rhino, and didn't return for the boosters like I told him."

"But..." she stammered. "These are valuable horses, and I thought you said you could keep them healthy!"

"I *could,* if you'd let me! You ignore my advice and prevent me from doing what you say you want done. Make up your mind! Either make the effort to take care of these horses, or quit complaining that veterinarians won't help you get what you want."

"Well... but what do we do about Silver now?"

"He has an upper respiratory infection, probably influenza, but I can't be sure. It also may be rhino, because he didn't get the full series of vaccines required to protect him. There are no medications to treat viral infections in horses, but if he's rested, he should recover on his own."

Little Cody piped up, "Are you telling me I can't ride my dad's horse! I can't rope on him this weekend in Kansas City?"

I don't know that I'd ever been so mad at a client before! The Filberts were raising their sons to disregard their horses' needs just as they did. Didn't anyone in this family care about these horses? Did they only care about the success the horses could bring them in the arena? Even if they had no compassion for the animals themselves, couldn't they understand that a healthy horse will compete better? If the Filberts had any common sense at all, they'd realize that healthy roping horses earn more money than sick horses - more than enough to pay for the vaccines!

"No. I'm not telling you that you can't ride your own horse. He's your horse. You have the legal right to do whatever you want with him. But you brought him here because you sought medical advice and treatment. Silver is sick - too sick to run fast in a rodeo. He'll probably be too slow to win you any money. And by the time you trailer him to Kansas City and back, he'll probably have pneumonia, as he did last time. The pneumonia may kill him - but he's your horse. It's your choice. You decide."

No wonder the Filberts couldn't get good veterinary care for their horses! They ignored the good advice they received and made the same mistakes over and over again. If they didn't believe me, couldn't they see for themselves that the same problems were recurring?

Unfortunately the horses suffered for their owners' ignorance and lack of compassion. Yet those same horses repeatedly put money into the Filberts' pockets. I did my best to help, but they refused to spend any money on the horses, and wouldn't change their management.

The Filberts put Silver back in the trailer and headed home. I don't know if they rested him, or took him to the roping, because I didn't hear from them for months. I assumed they were trying other veterinarians, looking for one who could keep their horses healthy for free by waving a magic wand.

The next time Harry Filbert called it was not for one of his horses, but for a friend's horse.

"Dr. Thibeault, one of our friends is in town for a ropin' and forgot to bring Bute for his horse. Can you help him out?"

Phenylbutazone, commonly called bute, is a pain reliever used in horses with arthritis or injuries. It's like aspirin for horses. Bute is a prescription drug, so only veterinarians, not feed stores, are authorized to dispense it. In order to dispense any prescription drugs, the veterinarian must first examine the horse, and determine that the horse needs the treatment. To sell bute without examining the horse is a violation of the Colorado Veterinary Medical Practice Act, putting the veterinarian's license in jeopardy.

"Sure, Harry, I can help your friend."

"Great!"

"When do you want to bring the horse by for an exam?"

"Uh, well… I don't want an exam. I just want the bute."

"Sorry. State law requires an examination before dispensing any prescription medications. I'll be glad to examine the horse for you."

"No thanks." Mr. Filbert hung up.

No doubt the Filberts had already tried ol' Doc Hastings.

That was the last time I ever heard from any of the Filberts.

Chapter 26 Just Rewards

As Rocky grazed, I sat on the carpet of fresh spring grass, basking in the soft, golden rays of dusk. I leaned back on the gray stone garden wall, reflecting on my journey.

Tomorrow I would achieve my final goal, officially opening my very own equine vet clinic on our farm. I had invited my clients and friends to share in our celebration. And I was surrounded by my supportive parents and my animals - Clancy and Rocky.

The bond that formed when I first set eyes on a horse never waned. I dedicated my life to these wonderful, inspiring creatures.

As I pursued my dream by working in the horse industry, I finally found my way on that foggy morning bicycle ride in Florida. It had been a long road - 20 years from the day I dropped out of college until opening day for my clinic.

And I finally had the farm I had dreamed of since childhood.

My journey took me through years of financial hardship and academic struggle, but it was a marvelous adventure. Today the struggles were pushed back to the farthest reaches of my memory.

I felt welcomed into the veterinary profession from the first day of vet school, where I got to know so many inspiring role models - talented and passionate veterinarians who helped me through the difficult courses - pushing me to be my best. And I was privileged to study with an eager class of students who have become my esteemed colleagues.

I felt proud to belong to such a wonderfully compassionate profession.

My life was immeasurably enriched by my growing list of clients - caring horsewomen like Cathie Ferrari and Barb Lewis, who staunchly support humane treatment of animals, and devote their lives to making it happen; Mary Wilkinson, who had a house full of rescue dogs that no one else wanted, and who lovingly cared for Popcorn, who flourished in her care, still going strong a decade beyond her life expectancy; Sherry Edmonds, who rescued hundreds of horses through Horse Helpers; The Simpsons, whose sense of humor delighted me; and the Palmers, who were sensible, honest, and competent horsemen who risked their lives protecting average citizens like me. They quickly earned my deepest respect.

The Filberts added dimension to my life in their own way.

I watched Sherry Orton and Jessie Berger blossom into good horsewomen, and I was happy to help them achieve their goals.

My beautiful equine patients so gently allowed me to do painful procedures when a single kick could have dispatched me. They caused me to grow as a horsewoman, and challenged me with difficult ailments. I had to reach deep within myself to help them.

Patients like Silver Queen and Patrick, who ignored their incurable diseases and lived their short lives to the fullest; Annie, who seemed to tell Bert about life from a horse's perspective, and Boxer, who added the unexpected to my life with his antics.

And even the dogs that somehow found their way into my horse practice, Boo and Emily, now were living the good life. They shared their spirits with me as they passed through my hands.

I couldn't imagine my life any other way. How empty would my life be without these wonderful people and their horses?

I'd do it all again in a heartbeat.

But it was growing dark, and the spring evening was turning cool. I climbed to my feet.

"Come on Rocky. We've got a busy day tomorrow."

Clancy rose to her feet and crouched behind Rocky's heels, eager to help him get to the barn. I tugged on his halter and Rocky begrudgingly raised his head. The three of us walked toward the paddock.

In the fading light, a great blue heron flapped its long wings overhead on its way home.